PLUMBING
AND HEATING

Other Macmillan Building Books

Painting and Decorating, third edition L. F. J. Tubb

Brush and Roller Painting Mike Ross

Brickwork and Associated Studies, volumes 1, 2 and 3 H. Bailey and
 D. W. Hancock

Building Maintenance Ivor H. Seeley

Building Technology Ivor H. Seeley

Carpentry, Joinery & Machine Woodworking, Wood Trades Part 1 A. B. Emary

Carpentry and Joinery, Wood Trades Part 2 A. B. Emary

Woodworking A. B. Emary

BASIC BUILDING SERIES

Plumbing and Heating

F. HALL, M.I.P.H.E., M.I.O.B.

Senior Lecturer, Building Services
Guildford County College of Technology
Silver Medallist, City and Guilds of London Institute

Illustrated by

A. L. MOSELEY, F.R.I.C.S., F.S.V.A.

Vice Principal
College of Estate Management London

Third Edition

First edition 1961
Reprinted 1962, 1965, 1967
SI edition 1970
Reprinted 1971, 1973
Third edition 1980
Reprinted 1981, 1982

Published by
THE MACMILLAN PRESS LTD
London and Basingstoke
Companies and representatives throughout the world

ISBN 0 333 29124 7

Printed in Hong Kong

Foreword

Recent revisions in the pattern of Building Education mark the biggest step forward that has taken place for almost thirty years, and in these changes it is right that training for craftsmanship should have been given a place of equal importance with that of technology and management.

It is intended that possession of the new City and Guilds of London Institute Craft Certificate shall denote that **a satisfactory** standard of competence in craftsmanship has been reached after (normally) three years of indentured apprenticeship including **attendance at** appropriate part-time day **and/or** evening classes at a Technical College.

It is not intended however that training should end at this stage and it is hoped that the keener and more able apprentice will continue his studies and obtain the Advanced Craft Certificate followed by the Full Technological Certificate of the City and Guilds Institute. Thereafter the way is open, through Foremanship studies or National Certificate Courses, to the examinations and professional qualifications of the Institute of Builders.

This series of books, largely consisting of simple notes and sketches in extension of lectures, should be of day-to-day assistance to Craft-Certificate students. Ancillary subjects such as Science and Calculations are treated separately and will probably be studied in this way at College, but they must **at all times** be considered as an integral part of the Trade Technology and related to that subject at the appropriate stage.

G.O. SWAYNE O.B.E., F.I.O.B.

Chairman, Southern Counties Regional
Joint Apprenticeship Committee

Preface

The primary aim of this book is to assist the plumbing student to reach the standard required for the theoretical examinations of the City and Guilds of London Institute Craft Certificate.

This third edition includes additional text on heating systems and gas appliances which are required under the new syllabus having a content common with the Heating and Ventilating Craft courses.

It should also be of assistance to students studying under the syllabus for Plumbing courses only, the Heating and Ventilating Craft courses and for the examinations set by the various Regional Examining Bodies.

Students in Building, Surveying and Architecture studying for the new Technician Education Council (TEC) Certificate and Diploma should also find the book useful as an introduction to services.

The book is not intended to cover the subjects completely, but to provide sufficient information to enable the students to grasp the basic principles, and then to extend this knowledge in practice and in the theory classes at the Technical Colleges. Whenever possible, the text has been illustrated, which helps to give a better understanding of the topics under consideration. In the preparation of this book, constant reference has been made to the new City and Guilds of London Institute Syllabus, British Standards Specifications, Codes of Practice and Regulations. The student is also advised to study technical information leaflets from the various manufacturers, trade journals and information provided by the Copper and Lead Development Associations.

Good opportunities exist for qualified plumbers and heating fitters and it is hoped that the student will carry on with his studies for the Advanced Craft Certificate.

F. HALL

Contents

Metrication in the Building Industry

In 1971, the Council of Ministers of the EEC decided to commit all member countries to amending their legislation regarding SI units (Système Internatio d'Unités). The United Kingdom had already decided that SI units would become the primary system of measurement and legislation is established in many countries.

SI UNITS

Although the plumbing student will now be using SI units it may assist if a list of units is given which may be referred to if doubt still exists. Also given are definitions and simple calculations. Use of symbols and scales for drawin have been added.

Quantity	SI Unit	Unit Symbol
Length	Metre	m
	Millimetre	mm
Area	Square metre	m^2
	Square millimetre	mm^2
Volume	Cubic metre	m^3
	Cubic millimetre	mm^3
Capacity	Litre	l
Mass	Kilogram	kg
Density	Kilograms per cubic metre	kg/m^3
Mass flow rate	Kilograms per second	kg/s
Volume flow rate	Cubic metres per second	m^3/s
Heat flow rate	Watt	W
Power	Watt	W
Energy	Joule	J
Force	Newton	N
Pressure and stress	Pascal (newton per square metre)	Pa
Calorific value	Kilojoules per cubic metre	kJ/m^3
Latent heat	Kilojoules per kilogram	kJ/kg
Absolute temperature	Kelvin	K
Normal temperature	Degree Celcius	°C
Temperature interval	Degree Celcius	°C
Time	Second	s
U Value	Watts per square metre per degree Celcius	$W/(m^2\ °C)$

MULTIPLES AND SUB-MULTIPLES OF SI UNITS

Multiplication factor		Prefix	Symbol
1 000 000	10^6	mega	M
1 000	10^3	kilo	k
100	10^2	hecto	h
10	10^1	deca	da
0.1	10^{-1}	deci	d
0.01	10^{-2}	centi	c
0.001	10^{-3}	milli	m
0.000 001	10^{-6}	micro	μ

MEANING OF TERMS

Newton Is that force which, when acting on a mass of one kilogram gives it an acceleration of one metre per second per second.

Joule Is the work done by a force of one newton when its point of application is moved through a distance of one metre in the direction of the force.

Watt is one joule per second.

Note $W = J/s = N\,m/s$

USE OF SYMBOLS

A space should be left between figures and symbols.

Examples   20.000 m (optional to use symbol).
20 mm (optional to use symbol)
20 m (always use symbol).

Whenever confusion could arise between number and linear dimensions, use symbol.

Examples   20.6 mm (always use symbol).
30 km (always use symbol).
8 m^2 (always use symbol).
8 m^3 (always use symbol).

DIMENSIONS ON DRAWINGS

One metre and over, to be written in metres to three places of decimals, e.g. 5.450

Under one metre to be written in millimetres only, e.g. 450

No symbols on dimensions on drawings unless decimals of mm e.g. 20.6 mm

Descriptions with single measurement should show symbol e.g. 3 mm sheet metal

Descriptions with two or more measurements need no symbol e.g. 51 × 25 timber battens

USEFUL NOTES

1 m^3 — 1000 litre
1 litre — 1 000 000 mm^3
1 litre of pure water = 1 kg
Pressure of water in Pa = head of water in metres × 1000 × 9.81
Pressure of water in kPa = head of water in metres × 9.81 or 10 approximately
Capacity of a tank in litres = length × breadth × depth in metres × 1000

Specific heat capacity of air = 1010 J/kg °C
Specific heat capacity of water = 4180 J/kg °C
Density of water = 1000 kg/m^3
Density of air = 1.20 kg/m^3
Boiler power = mass flow rate in kg/s × temperature rise in °C × specific heat capacity of water in J/kg °C. (see page 81).

CALCULATIONS

A tank measures 1.5 m × 900 mm × 700 mm. Calculate the volume in m^3 and capacity in litres.

Volume	= 1.5 m × 900 mm × 700 mm
	= 1.5 × 0.9 × 0.7
	= 0.945 m^3
1 m^3	= 1000 litres
∴ capacity	= 0.945 × 1000
	= 945 litres

Calculate the pressure of water in Pa when the head is 15 metres

1 m^3 of water has a mass of 1000 kg. ∴ pressure over an area of 1 m^2 will equal 15 × 1000 × 9.81 = 147150 Pa or 147.150 kPa

METRIC SCALES FOR DRAWING

Detail drawings
  1 : 1
  1 : 5
  1 : 10
  1 : 20
Constructional plans, elevations and sections
  1 : 50
  1 : 100
  1 : 200
Layout and site plans
  1 : 500
  1 : 1250
  1 : 2500

To find the missing dimension in millimetres with the metric rule. Multiply this by the scale and the result equals the missing dimension.

To find the missing scale in millimetres with the metric rule. Divide the marked dimension by the measured dimension (but make marked dimension into whole numbers). Result equals the scale.

TYPES OF COPPER TUBES

B.S. 2871: Part 1

Table X — Half hard bendable copper tube for hot and cold domestic water and heating services.

Table Y — Fully annealed tube for underground services.

Table Z — Hard drawn thin wall tube for hot and cold domestic water and heating services.

The outside diameters of the tubes in millimetres are as follows:
6, 8, 10, 12, 15, 18, 22, 28, 35, 42, 54, 76.1, 108, 133, 159

CONVERSION FACTORS

Although it is unnecessary to waste time in laborious conversion exercises, it may help the student to become familiar with the values in SI Units, in the early stages, if he can see the equivalent in Imperial Units.

to convert	into	multiply by
pounds force	newtons	4.45
kilograms force	newtons	9.81
tons force	kilonewtons	9.96
pounds per sq inch pressure	newtons per square metre	6894.76
tons per sq ft pressure	kilonewtons per square metre	107.25
inches of water	newtons per square metre	249
feet of water	newtons per square metre	2989
feet per second	metres per second	0.3048
feet per minute	millimetres per second	5.08
miles per hour	metres per second	0.447
miles per hour	kilometres per hour	1.61
acceleration in feet per second^2	metres per second^2	0.3048
calorific value in Btu/ft^3	kilojoules per cubic metre	37.3
Btu/lb	kilojoules per kilogram	2.33

EQUIVALENT VALUES OF SI UNITS

Length
1 mile = 1.609 34 km
1 yard = 0.914 4 m
1 foot = 0.304 8 m
1 inch = 25.4 mm

Area
1 yd^2 = 0.836 127 m^2
1 ft^2 = 0.092 903 0 m^2
1 in.^{2} = 645.16 mm^2
1 in.^{2} = 6.451 6 cm^2

Volume
1 yd^3 = 0.764 555 m^3
1 ft^3 = 28.316 8 dm^3
1 in^3 = 16.387 1 cm^3

Capacity
1 quart = 1.137 litre
1 pint = 0.568 litre
1 gallon = 4.546 litre

Density
1 ton yd^3 = 1328.94 kg/m^3
1 lb/ft^3 = 16.0185 kg/m^3
1 lb/in^3 = 27.679 9 g/cm^3

Force
1 ton f = 9.964 02 kN
1 lb f = 4.448 N

Mass per unit area
1 lb/in^2 = 703.070 kg/m^2

Mass
1 ton = 1016.05 kg
1 cwt = 50.8023 kg
1 lb = 0.453 593 kg

Calorific value
1 Btu/ft^3 = 37.2589 kJ/m^3

Pressure
1 lb/in.^{2} = 6894.76 Pa

Energy
1 therm = 105.506 MJ

Heat flowrate
1 Btu/h = 0.293 W
1 Btu/ft^2/h = 3.1546 W/m^2 °C

Power
1 horsepower = 746.700 W

Heat energy
1 Btu = 1.055 kJ

Velocity
1 mile/h = 1.6093 km/h
1 ft/s = 0.3048 m/s

Temperature
°C = 5/9 (°F − 32)
°F = 9/5 (°C + 32)

ROUGH EQUIVALENTS

1 yard	= 0.9 metre
0.040 in.	= 1 millimetre
$\frac{5}{8}$ mile	= 1 kilometre
1 cwt	= 51 kilograms
1 ton force	= 10 kilonewtons
1 lb force	= 4.5 kilonewtons
2 lb	= 1 kilogram
1 cubic yard	= 0.75 cubic metre
100 cubic ft	= 3 cubic metre
30 m.p.h.	= 50 km per hour
70 m.p.h.	= 120 km per hour
1 Btu	= 1 kilojoule
10 Btu/h	= 3 watts = 3 joules/second
1 therm	= 105 megajoules
10 gallons	= 45 litres
2 pints	= 1 litre
100 lb/in.^{2}	= 700 kPa or 700 kN/m^2 or 7 bar
1 ton/in.^{2}	= 15 MPa or 1.5 hectobar
1 horsepower	= 746 W = 746 J/s

THICKNESSES OF SHEET METALS

The SI system recommends the use of the millimetre for the thicknesses of sheet metals and these thicknesses have been used in the book.

The B.S. 1178 Code No. 3 recommends that for sheet lead a code number should be used which corresponds to the old Imperial weights in pounds per square foot. A Standard for sheet copper has not yet been published but it ma also be possible for a code number to be used corresponding to the old standard wire gauge (s.w.g.).

Sheet lead		Sheet copper	
B.S. Code No	Thickness mm	S.w.g.	Thickness mm
3	1.25	20	0.914
4	1.80	21	0.813
5	2.24	22	0.711
6	2.50	23	0.610
7	3.15	24	0.559
8	3.55	26	0.457

Sheet lead carries colour markings as follows

Code No 3 = Green	Code No 6 = Black
Code No 4 = Blue	Code No 7 = White
Code No 5 = Red	Code No 8 = Orange

Physical Properties and uses of Metal used in Plumbing

The physical properties of a metal refer to its mechanical properties, i.e. its weight, colour, strength, etc.

MEANING OF PROPERTIES

Density is the weight or mass per unit volume, e.g. kg/m^3. Ductility is the property that allows a metal to be drawn out into a fine wire.

Elasticity is the property that allows a metal to return to its original shape after it has been deformed by force, e.g. a piece of elastic when stretched will return to its original length when the tensional force is released.

Hardness is the ability of a metal to withstand scratching or wear.

Durability is the ability to resist corrosion from water, air, acids etc.

Malleability is the property that allows a metal to be hammered or rolled into thin sheets without fracture.

Plasticity is the property exactly opposite to elasticity. A plastic metal does not return to its original shape when deformed by force.

Tensile Strength is the force required to pull a metal asunder. The value is expressed in MPa.

Specific heat capacity of a metal is the amount of heat in Joules required to increase the temperature of 1 kg mass of a metal through 1 °C.

Chemical Symbol is the symbol used in chemistry and is a useful abbreviation for a metal.

Melting Point is the temperature when a metal changes from a solid to a liquid

Lead is a soft, heavy metal, bluish grey in colour, very plastic and easily cut. It has a bright metallic lustre when freshly cut or shaved but rapidly tarnishes on exposure to air. Lead is extremely durable and will resist corrosion by most acids. Uses—in sheet form for the covering and weathering of roofs and in pipe form for water, gas, soil, vent, waste and rainwater pipes.

Copper is reddish brown in colour and when clean has a bright metallic lustre It is very ductile and malleable, being next only to gold, silver and platinum. It is very elastic being second only to steel and is also very durable and resistant to corrosion attack by most acids. It is an excellent conductor of heat. Copper hardens on working but can be annealed or softened by heating to redness and cooling either in air or water. The popular idea that copper has to be quenched in water to anneal is incorrect. Uses—As described for lead, and for the manufacture of cylinders, boilers and geysers. Copper is also used extensively for making alloys such as brass and bronze.

Aluminium is a bluish white metal and is by far the lightest of the common metals. It is very durable in normal atmospheric conditions but is readily attacked in sulphurous atmospheres. Pure aluminium is soft, malleable and ductile, but hardens on working; it can be annealed by heating and cooling in air or water. The addition of other metals to form an aluminium alloy converts it into a hard, strong alloy, which can be used for structural purposes. Uses—in sheet form (Super purity 99. 99 per cent) for covering and weathering roofs. Aluminium alloy is used for eaves gutters, rainwater pipes, lavatory basins, sinks and basin and sink brackets.

Zinc is a bluish white metal with a bright metallic lustre. It is brittle when

1

ld but malleable when heated to about 93 °C. It is readily attacked by some
aters and by the sulphurous atmosphere in industrial towns. Uses—in sheet
rm for covering and weathering to roofs, eaves gutters and rainwater pipes.
so for protecting steel and iron in the form of galvanising or sherardising
d for making such alloys as brass.

in is a hard silvery white lustrous metal with a crystalline structure. A
aracteristic of the metal is a cracking sound that can be easily heard when
thin bar of tin is held close to the ear and bent. This is caused by the de-
rmation of the crystals. Tin is an extremely durable metal and is not affected
the air or water, is ductile but not very strong. Uses—As a protective coat-
g to copper geysers, wash boilers, tea urns and for many types of copper and
eel receptacles. In soft water districts tin is used for protecting lead pipes,
ther in the form of a lining or washing and it is used extensively for alloying
ith other metals to make solder and bronzes.

on—pure iron is a soft metal possessing good malleability and ductility. In
is form however, it has few practical uses.

ast Iron—in this form it is used extensively for plumbing. Cast iron contains
mall amounts of carbon, phosphorus, sulphur and manganese. The carbon
.5 to 4 per cent) makes cast iron hard and brittle but it is an extremely fluid
etal when molten and can be cast into intricate shapes. Cast iron is grey in
olour (due to the carbon present) with a crystalline structure. It does not
orrode as rapidly as steel when exposed to air or water but some form of
rotection is required. Uses—for the manufacture of baths, boilers, cisterns,
ater and gas mains, soil, vent, rainwater and drain pipes, gutters etc.

ABLE OF PROPERTIES

Ietal	Chemical Symbol	Melting Point °C	Density kg/m³	Tensile Strength MPa (mega-pascal)	Coefficient of Linear Expansion °C
ead	Pb	327	11360	15.50	0.000029
opper	Cu	1083	8880	216.22 − 401.55	0.000017
luminium	Al	658	2720	61.777 − 100.366	0.000026
inc	Zn	412	7120	154.443 − 185.331	0.000029
in	Sn	228	7280	23.16	0.000021
ron	Fe	1200	7200	247.11 − 308.89	0.0000106

Soldering

Soft solders are true alloys being composed of lead and tin of varying proportions, and with or without a small percentage of antimony, (antimonial and non antimonial solders). Solder is used to join metal with a higher melting point.

The plumber uses solder for a variety of purposes, the type depending upon the type of work to be carried out.

Soft solders are classified by the B.S.S. 219 and the plumber uses three grades A, B and D.

TABLE OF SOLDERS AND THEIR USES

B.S. Grade A—Blowpipe solder

Composition	Melting Point (approximate)	Uses
34 per cent lead, 65 per cent tin, up to 1 per cent antimony. Approximately 2 tin : 1 lead	183°C	Gas pipe joints and capillary joints on copper pipes, Fig. 1.

B.S. Grade B—Tinman's solder

Composition	Melting Point (approximate)	Uses
48 per cent lead, 50 per cent tin, 2-3 per cent antimony. Approximately 1 tin : 1 lead	195°C	Tinning linings and all types of copper bitwork, Fig. 2.

B.S. Grade D—Plumbers' Solder

Composition	Melting Point (approximate)	Uses
68 per cent lead, 30 per cent tin, up to 2 per cent antimony. Approximately 1 tin : 2 lead	216°C	Wiped joints, Fig. 3.

Plastic Range If we melt different types of solder in a ladle and remove the heat, it will be noticed that some solders set quicker than others. There is a

3

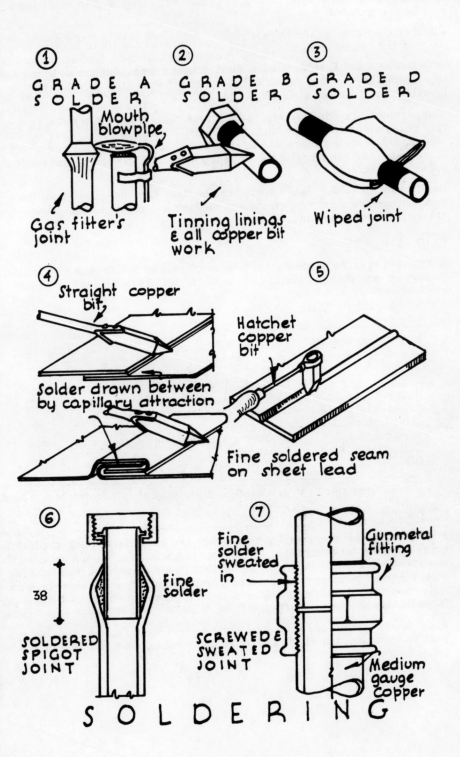

① GRADE A SOLDER

Gas fitter's joint

② GRADE B SOLDER

Mouth blowpipe

Tinning linings & all copper bit work

③ GRADE D SOLDER

Wiped joint

④ Straight copper bit

Solder drawn between by capillary attraction

⑤ Hatchet copper bit

Fine soldered seam on sheet lead

⑥ 38 | Fine solder

SOLDERED SPIGOT JOINT

⑦ Fine solder sweated in

Gunmetal fitting

SCREWED & SWEATED JOINT

Medium gauge copper

SOLDERING

range of temperature where the solder is neither solid nor liquid known as 'the plastic range'. The length of time solder remains in this pasty or plastic state after heat has been removed, determines the degree with which the solder may be manipulated.

Plumbers' solder has the longest plastic range and it is during this time that the plumber 'wipes' his joint.

Both Grade A and B solders have short plastic ranges and cannot be used for wiped joints, but as they set quickly they enable joints to be made which can be used almost immediately after making.

Temperature of solder for wiping A simple method used to test the temperature of plumbing solder for wiping is to push a piece of white paper into the solder. If the solder chars this to dark brown, the temperature is correct. If the paper catches fire the solder is too hot, and if the paper chars only light brown it is too cold.

Purification of solder When solder has become dirty due to the addition of bench droppings, it may be cleaned by melting in a metal pot and adding zinc chloride or sal-ammoniac.

FLUXES

A flux serves three purposes, (a) to prevent oxidisation, (b) to help the solder to alloy or mix with the surface of the metal, (c) to help the solder to flow.

TABLE OF FLUXES

Traditional Flux	For Soldering
Tallow	Lead with Plumbing solder
Resin	Lead with fine solder, brass, copper, gunmetal.
Hydrochloric Acid	Zinc (not cleaned)
Killed spirits (Zinc Chloride)	Zinc (cleaned), copper, brass, iron, steel.
Sal-ammoniac	Brass, copper, gunmetal, steel (tinning copper bits).
Gallipoli or Olive Oil	Pewter

Note—Killed spirits is produced by dissolving zinc in hydrochloric acid.

SOLDERING

In order to solder successfully, four things are essential, (a) correct flux, (b) correct solder, (c) cleanliness, (d) correct temperature. Having obtained these requirements, the flux is applied to the thoroughly cleaned surface, and the solder applied by means of a soldering iron. Capillary attraction plays an important part in soldering; solder will draw between two cleaned metal surfaces by this phenomenon. (Fig. 4).

Fig. 5 shows method of forming a seam on sheet lead, Fig. 6 a soldered spigot joint on lead pipe, and Fig. 7 a screwed and sweated soldered joint on medium gauge copper pipe.

URFACE AREAS

Rectangle = base × height or length × breadth

Parallelogram = base × perpendicular height

Trapezoid = half sum of parallel sides × perpendicular distance between

$$= \frac{a + b}{2} \times h$$

Triangle = half base × perpendicular height $= \frac{b \times h}{2}$

Circle $= \pi R^2$ or $0.7854D^2$ $(\pi = 3.1416)$

Annulus $= \pi(R^2 - r^2) = \pi(R - r)(R + r)$

Ellipse $= \pi ab$ where a and b are half the lengths of the long and short axes

Sector of circle $= \frac{\theta}{360} \pi R^2$ where θ is angle subtended at centre of circle

Segment of circle = area of sector − area of triangle

Sphere $= 4\pi R^2$

Cone and Pyramid $= \left(\text{slant height} \times \frac{\text{perimeter of base}}{2} \right) + \text{area of base}$

VOLUMES

Rectangular prism = length × breadth × height

Cylinder = area of base × height $= \pi R^2 \times h$

Cone = area of base × $\frac{1}{3}$ perpendicular height $= \pi R^2 \times \frac{h}{3}$

Pyramid = area of base × $\frac{1}{3}$ perpendicular height

Sphere $= \frac{4}{3} \pi R^3$ or $\frac{\pi D^3}{6}$

PERIMETERS

Square = 4 × length of one side

Rectangle = (2 × long side) + (2 × short side)

Triangle = sum of lengths of each side

Circle $= 2\pi R$ or πD

Arc of circle $= \frac{\theta}{360} \times 2\pi R$ where θ is angle subtended at centre of circle

Ellipse $= \pi(a + b)$ where a and b are half the lengths of the long and short axes

6

Wooden Tools for Sheet Metal Roof Work

To prevent damage to sheet metals when bossing or dressing, wooden tools are essential. The wood used is normally Beech or Boxwood, although Holly, Horn-beam or Lignum Vitae may also be used.

The surface of wooden tools must be kept perfectly smooth so that the sheet metal is not marked. They must therefore never be struck by steel tools, and must be kept separate from them. When used outside, a regular soaking in raw linseed oil will prevent any warping or splitting of the wood when left unpro-tected from the weather.

The edges of wooden tools must be slightly rounded to prevent damage to the metals. When selecting wooden tools it is important to examine them for any flaws to the edges, and also to see that they are of the correct shape and size for the particular work in hand.

Frequently excellent wooden tools are made by plumbers themselves, who vary their designs to suit their own particular taste and requirements. An apprentice would be well advised to make some of the tools he will require from well seasoned pieces of suitable wood.

Flat Dresser Fig. 1—used to dress sheet metals to a flat surface, prior to set-ting out, and also for dressing up on completion of work. The handle should give ample clearance for the knuckles, and one side should be set over to pro-vide a 'setting in' edge. This enables the sheet metal to be dressed up against a corner.

Bossing Mallet Fig. 2—for bossing or working to a required shape. The malacca cane handle gives a slight spring when striking sheet metals. The pear shaped head is usually of boxwood.

Mallet Fig. 3—used for striking the 'setting in' stick or chase wedge or flat dresser, and for forming lock welts in sheet copper or aluminium. It has a boxwood head and a malacca cane handle.

Bossing Stick Fig. 4—used to boss sheet lead.

Bending Stick Fig. 5—although used primarily for bending lead pipes the tool is also very useful for bossing.

Setting-in stick Fig. 6—used to set-in creases in sheet lead, the tool being struck with the mallet.

Step Turner Fig. 7—used to turn the steps of flashings for fixing into the brick joints.

Chase wedge Fig. 8—used to set in creases in sheet lead where there is not room for the setting-in stick, and also for squaring up sheet metals on completion.

USING WOODEN TOOLS

The greatest care should be taken when using wooden tools as careless use will soon damage the edges or split the wood. When a large sheet of metal has to be dressed to a level surface prior to setting out the work, a sheet lead 'flapper' will do the job instead of the dresser and so save damage to the latter.

Students tend to strike sheet metal too hard, hoping to finish the work at greater speed. It is however essential to first study the work and then by steady blows directed where required, work the metal to the required shape.

The tools described are used for working sheet lead, copper, zinc or aluminium

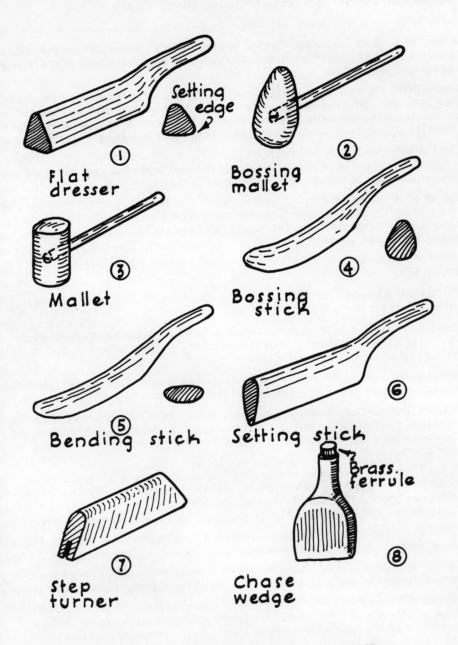

① Flat dresser — Setting edge

② Bossing mallet

③ Mallet

④ Bossing stick

⑤ Bending stick

⑥ Setting stick

⑦ Step turner

⑧ Chase wedge — Brass ferrule

WOODEN TOOLS FOR SHEET METAL ROOFWORK

Tools for Lead Pipe Work

Rasp Fig.1 Made from cast steel, it is similar to a file but has coarse teeth. The tool should never be used without a handle. Used for squaring and tapering the ends of lead pipes.

Shave Hook Fig.2 A steel heart shaped blade with a cutting edge is rivetted to a steel rod. To prevent the wooden handle from pulling off, the steel rod passes through the handle and the end of the rod is rivetted over a washer. Used for shaving the ends of lead pipes clean prior to fluxing and tinning.

Bent bolt or pin Fig.3 Made from a piece of 13 mm diameter steel rod about 305 mm long, bent at both ends as shown, one end being tapered. Used for the preparation of branch and knuckle bends.

Auger or pipe opener Fig.4 The steel base of the tool is conical in shape and has two cutting edges. To prevent the wooden handle from twisting off, the square stem passes through the handle. Used to cut holes in lead pipes in preparing branch joints.

Mandril Fig.5 Made from boxwood or lignum vitae. Used to remove dents in lead pipes.

Turnpin or Tampin Fig.6 A cone shaped tool made from boxwood or lignum vitae. Used for opening the ends of lead pipes.

Scribing Plate Fig.7 A brass plate with holes at regular intervals down the centre is shaped as shown. Used for scribing the shape of branch and knuckle joints in conjunction with the dividers.

Dividers or compasses Fig.8 Two steel points are rivetted together, the position of the points being fixed by means of a wing nut.

Wiping Cloths Fig.9 These are made from fustian, a coarse heavy cloth made of cotton and flax. Plumbers know the cloth as 'moleskin'. For underhand joints the width of the cloth is 15 mm wider than the joint and between 102 mm and 127 mm long.

A thick piece of cardboard is inserted between the layers to form a core; this core gives the cloth its necessary shape. The branch cloth does not require a cardboard core. The size of this cloth is 102 mm × 38 mm for joints on pipes up to 25 mm diameter and 102 mm × 76 mm for larger diameter pipes.

Cloths require at least six thicknesses, and it is important to see that the 'grain' runs along the length of the cloth.

Before the cloth is used, chalk is rubbed into the surface and tallow applied where contact is made with the solder. Used for making wiped solder joints.

Bending Spring Fig.10 Made from steel. The spring is inserted in the lead pipe and the pipe bent to an angle slightly greater than required. Before withdrawing the spring, the bend is opened to the required angle.

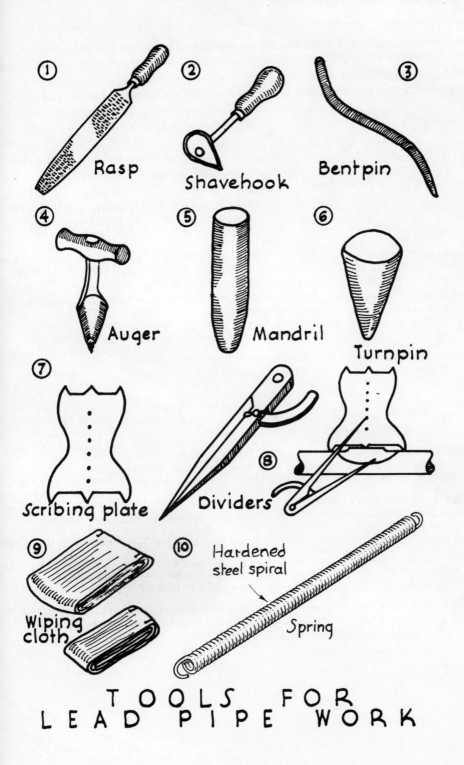

① Rasp

② Shavehook

③ Bentpin

④ Auger

⑤ Mandril

⑥ Turnpin

⑦ Scribing plate

⑧ Dividers

⑨ Wiping cloth

⑩ Hardened steel spiral

Spring

TOOLS FOR
LEAD PIPE WORK

Tools for Mild Steel Pipe Work

The tools required are hand die stocks, wheel cutters, reamers, hack saws, pipe wrenches and pipe vice.

Hand die stocks Fig.1 shows a ratchet receder die stock, and various sizes may be obtained for threading pipes from 6 mm to 100 mm diameter.

The quick release lever allows the dies to 'recede' from the pipe, thus enabling the tool to be removed from the pipe without reversing.

The ratchet makes the work much easier than with the solid die stock as the correct position for threading can be maintained. The thread should be cut so that the fitting can be screwed up hand-tight for about two thirds of the thread. A slack fit will cause a leaky joint.

On large jobs pipes may be threaded by means of a portable electric or petrol driven screwing machine and a good deal of labour will be saved by using this method.

Wheel cutters Fig.2 These may be obtained with three cutting wheels or with one cutting wheel and two rollers. The former type is useful for cutting pipe in situ where it is impossible to move the cutter through a full turn. The latter type is preferable for cutting pipe on the bench. The two broad steel rollers assist in aligning the tool-steel cutting wheel and will also remove the burr which would otherwise be made on the outside of the pipe. Note: Machine oil must be applied whilst cutting and screwing is in progress.

Reamers Fig.3 These are used to remove the burr from the inside of the pipe. The reamer may be turned by a tommy-bar or hand brace. A round file may also be used for removing the burr.

Hacksaws, Fig.4 These may be either adjustable, straight or pistol grip handle types. For cutting steel the blade should be flexible tungsten steel type, 229, 254 or 305 mm long with 24 teeth to 25 mm.

The blade should be tightened in the frame by the wing nut so that the blade is in tension and makes a musical note when plucked. The blade should be kept horizontal when cutting and the full length of the blade used.

Pipe wrenches Fig.5 These may be either 'Stillson' or chain type. Various sizes may be obtained, the overall length depending upon the diameter of the pipe to be tightened, e.g. 'Stillsons' 256 mm long are for pipes up to 38 mm diameter, 460 mm up to 50 mm diameter, and 1.219 m up to 127 mm diameter.

The correct size of wrench must always be used, as the practice of adding extr leverage by pushing a piece of pipe over the handle of a wrench too small for the pipe, exerts unnecessary strain on the tool.

Pipe vice, Fig.6 Various types may be obtained but the chain type shown is the most useful for the plumber, as it is very compact, readily fixed to the bench, and may be carried in the tool bag.

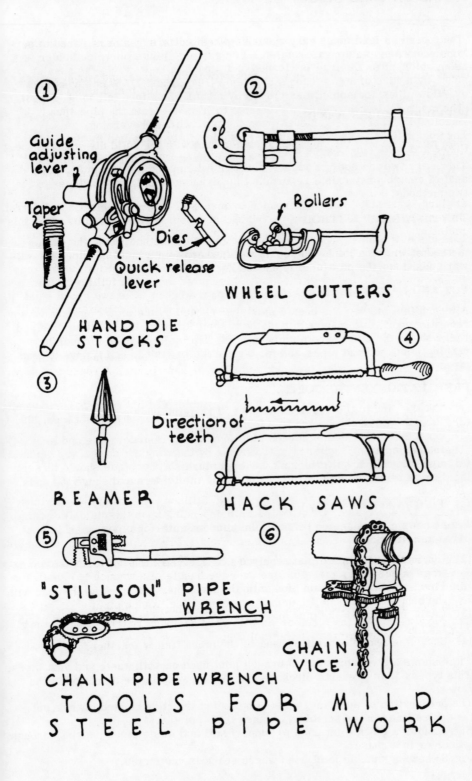

① Guide adjusting lever
Taper
Dies
Quick release lever
HAND DIE STOCKS

② Rollers
WHEEL CUTTERS

③ REAMER

④ Direction of teeth
HACK SAWS

⑤ "STILLSON" PIPE WRENCH

CHAIN PIPE WRENCH

⑥ CHAIN VICE

TOOLS FOR MILD STEEL PIPE WORK

Joints on Lead Pipes

Joints used on lead pipes vary according to the duty they are required to perform, i.e. water, waste, gas, vent etc. For gas pipe joints blowpipe solder is used, which, after the lead is cleaned and fluxed, is melted into the annular space by means of a gas fitter's blowlamp (Figs. 1 and 2). Waste, vent and overflow pipes are sometimes jointed by means of a wiped taft joint (Fig. 3).

WIPED PLUMBERS JOINTS

The solder used is known as plumbers solder, fully explained in 'Solders, fluxes and soldering', pages 3-5.

There are two methods of wiping joints: blowlamp and pot and ladle. A good deal of controversy exists regarding the advantages and disadvantages of the two methods.

THE BLOWLAMP METHOD

This has now almost superseded the pot and ladle method, being the easier method of wiping a joint. On repair work, where joints must be wiped in awkward positions, the blowlamp is especially suitable.

POT AND LADLE METHOD

Although this method has been almost superseded by the blowlamp method, for repetition work in the shop, this method is quicker than the blowlamp method. Fig. 4 shows the underhand plumbers joint. This joint is used for making running joints on lead pipes, and for connecting brass cap and linings to lead pipes etc.

PREPARATION OF THE JOINT

(1) Cut the pipe to the required length and rasp the ends square.
(2) Rasp down the closed end to a feather edge.
(3) Open the socket end by means of a turnpin and rasp down the end to a feather edge.
(4) Rub the ends down with chalk and apply tarnish.
(5) Scribe round the pipe by means of a pair of dividers and shave the ends clean.
(6) Fit the two ends firmly together and apply tallow.

Fig. 5 shows a right angled branch joint used on waterpipe. The joint is prepared as follows:

(1) Cut the branch pipe to the required length, square the end and rasp down to a feather edge.
(2) Form a hole in the main pipe with a pipe-opener and work up the lead with the bent-bolt and small hammer, to receive the branch pipe.
(3) Chalk and tarnish the pipe and scribe by means of the dividers and scribing plate.
(4) Shave the lead clean, tallow, and fit the pipes firmly together.

Fig. 6 shows a swept or splayed branch joint used on soil, waste and vent pipes. This type of joint prevents blockage due to the sweep in the direction of the flow.

The preparation of the joint is the same as for the right-angled branch, but the centre line for the scribing, is taken from point A.

Fig. 7 shows a block joint used to support soil and waste pipes passing through a floor or in a chase.

Fig. 8 shows a knuckle joint used where space is restricted.

13

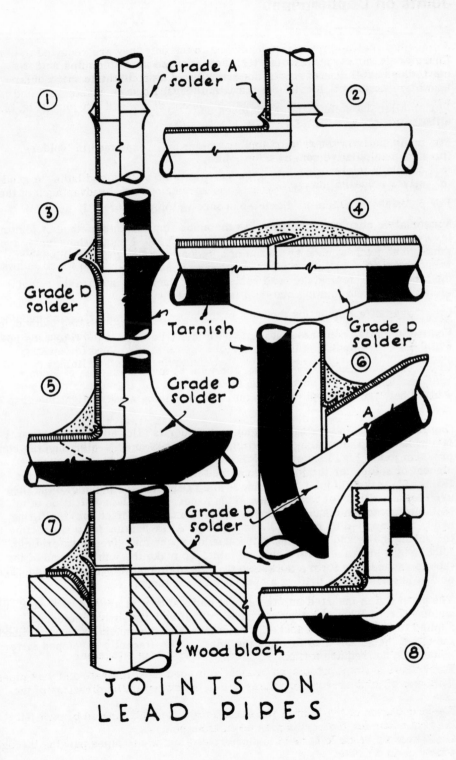

① ② Grade A solder

③ Grade D solder

④ Tarnish Grade D solder

⑤ Grade D solder

⑥ A

Grade D solder

⑦ Wood block

⑧

JOINTS ON LEAD PIPES

Joints on Copper Pipes

There are a variety of ways in which copper pipes may be jointed, and the method used will depend on: (a) the diameter of pipe; (b) the function of pipe, i.e water, waste, soil, etc; (c) the Local Authorities bylaws.

For smaller diameter light gauge pipes up to 50 mm the methods used are either:

(a) manipulative compression joints;
(b) non-manipulative compression joints;
(c) capillary joints, or
(d) silver soldered joints.

For pipes above 50 mm in diameter bronze welding is normally used.

Manipulative compression joints As the name implies, this method of jointing involves the manipulation of the end of the pipe. Fig. 1 shows the Kingley type joints. The joint is made by means of a special beading tool supplied by the manufacturers. The tool is inserted into the end of the pipe raising a bead on the tube. On tightening, the bead rests against the fitting and makes a metal to metal joint, and jointing material is then not required.

Other ways of manipulating the ends of the pipes includes flaring and cupping.

Non manipulative compression joint With this type of joint the tube ends remain and no manipulation is necessary.

Fig. 2 shows the Buttrix type joint. The joint is made by means of a copper compression cone. By screwing up the hexagonal nut, the copper cone is wedged between the nipple and the nut, thus providing a water-tight metal to metal joint.

Capillary Joints In making this joint soft solder is allowed to flow (by capillarity) between the tube and the fitting. The joint is much neater than the compression joint. Fig. 3 shows the Yorkshire type joint, in which the required amount of solder for the joint is contained in a groove machined inside the fitting. To make the joint, the inside of the fitting and the outside of the tube are cleaned with steel wool or fine glass paper. After the application of a suitable flux to the cleaned surfaces the tube end is inserted into the fitting, and heat is applied by means of a blow lamp. After heating for a short time, the solder melts and flows round the annular space and gives a water-tight joint. Fig. 4 shows a silver soldered joint. To make the joint, one end of the tube is expanded to form a socket so that the plain end fits tightly inside. The socket is formed by a drift of a special tube expander.

The plain end is inserted into the socket end and heat is applied by means of a welding torch. When the copper reaches a dull red heat, silver solder is applied to the edge of the socket. The solder fills the annular space and floods the top of the socket thus forming the joint. Note—Recently developed silver solders do not require a flux.

"KINGLEY" JOINT

Brass ring →   Copper pipe
                beaded

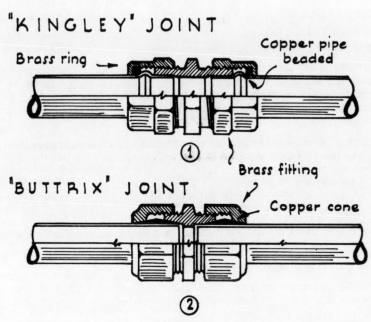

①

Brass fitting

"BUTTRIX" JOINT

Copper cone

②

"YORKSHIRE" (COPPER) JOINT

Fine solder

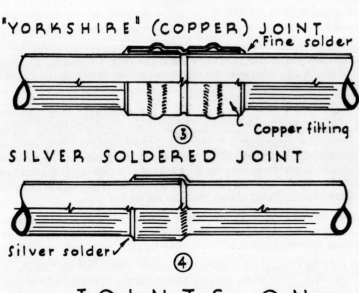

③

Copper fitting

SILVER SOLDERED JOINT

④

Silver solder ↙

JOINTS ON
COPPER PIPES

Joints on Mild Steel Pipes

Mild steel or wrought iron pipes may be jointed by one of the following methods:

(a) screwed joints with special fittings;
(b) autogenous welded joints;
(c) flanged joints.

Screwed Joints This method is used for small or large diameter pipes and is the most usual method of jointing. To make the joint, the pipe is cut to length and tapered thread is made at the end of the pipe just long enough to be housed in the fitting. The thread should not be cut too deep or a slack leaky joint will result.

Stranded hemp is wrapped round the thread in a clockwise manner, and graphite or a proprietory jointing paste is applied by means of a brush. The thread is then screwed into the fitting or vice versa and is tightened up by means of a 'Stillson' pipe wrench. The hemp and jointing material enter the threads and ensure a sound joint (hemp should not be used for jointing steam pipes as it burns away leaving a leaky joint). P.T.F.E. tape may also be used (see p. 154).

Fig. 1 shows a straight socket joint used for connecting together lengths of pipe.

Fig. 2 shows a variety of screwed fittings.

Fig. 3 shows a connector or longscrew used for making a joint where both ends of the pipe are fixed, e.g connections to tanks, boilers or geysers, and insertion of tees etc in existing pipe lines.

Fig. 4 shows a union joint, used for the same purpose as the connector, but it is quicker and easier to make. The joint can also be readily disconnected and remade.

Autogenous welded joints, fig. 5 This means the true welding of pipes, i.e. the filler rod and pipes are of the same material and both are melted together to form a weld.

This method of jointing is usually used on pipes 32 mm in diameter and over, but it is difficult to make alterations or additions when the installation is complete.

With a skilled welder, the joint is stronger than the pipe and the operation is both cheaper and quicker than screwed jointing. In making the joint it is essential that good penetration is made and that the weld is given some reinforcement by building up the bead above the outside of the pipe.

Flanged joints, fig. 6 This is an excellent method of jointing large diameter pipes both in boiler houses where easy dismantling is required and for high pressure steam or waterpipes.

The flanges may be of cast of malleable iron or steel and may be screwed to the ends of the pipe. The usual ring is made from corrugated brass known as the 'Taylors' ring.

17

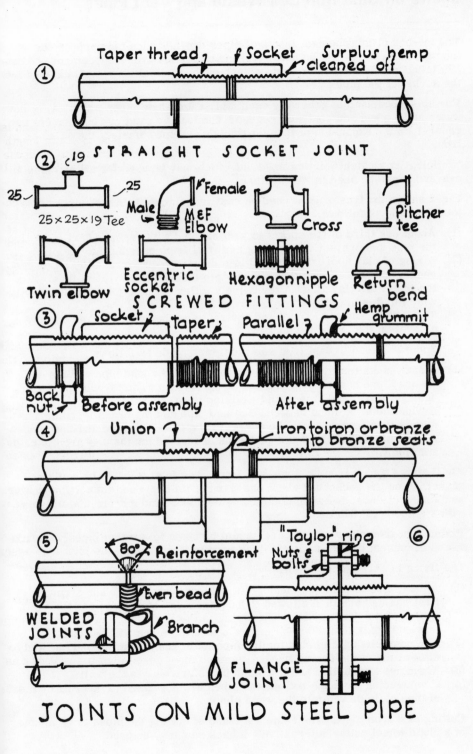

① Taper thread, Socket, Surplus hemp cleaned off

STRAIGHT SOCKET JOINT

② 25 — 19 — 25
25×25×19 Tee

Male — Female M&F Elbow

Cross

Pitcher tee

Twin elbow

Eccentric socket

Hexagon nipple

Return bend

SCREWED FITTINGS

③ Socket, Taper, Parallel, Hemp grummit

Back nut — Before assembly — After assembly

④ Union, Iron to iron or bronze to bronze seats

⑤ 80° Reinforcement
Even bead
Branch
WELDED JOINTS

⑥ "Taylor" ring
Nuts & bolts
FLANGE JOINT

JOINTS ON MILD STEEL PIPE

Joints on Cast Iron Soil Waste and Vent Pipes

The method of jointing cast iron soil pipes depends upon the purpose for which the pipe is to be used. The usual jointing materials are: lead, cement and sand 'Philplug', red lead putty or rust cement; each material being well caulked into the socket of the pipe.

For soil pipes, lead is generally used, whilst for waste pipes which carry hot water and expand and contract, red lead, cement and sand or rust cement are general, as the expansion of these materials is approximately the same as cast iron.

'Philplug' is a patent jointing material which may be used for all circumstances, and it can be used in wet weather.

Fig. 1 shows the type of joint used on cast iron to cast iron soil pipes. The joint is made as follows.

(1). About one third of the socket is well caulked with gasket. This is to align the pipe and prevent the jointing material from passing into the pipe.
(2). A ring of clay approximately 13 mm deep is bedded round the top of the socket and molten lead then poured into the socket until it is level with the top of the clay ring. Alternatively a flexible pipe jointing clip may be used for this purpose.
(3). The lead is allowed to cool and contract and then well caulked up leaving a bevel on the top of the socket.

Fig. 2 shows a lead to cast iron soil pipe joint, made as follows:

(1). A cast brass ferrule is fitted over the end of the lead pipe and the end of the lead pipe beaded over the end of the ferrule. The ferrule prevents damage to the lead pipe whilst caulking is carried out.
(2). A wiped joint is made between the lead pipe and the brass ferrule. The pipe is then inserted into the socket of the case iron pipe and the joint made with caulked lead and gasket as described for the cast iron to cast iron joint.

Fig. 3 shows a cast iron to stoneware joint. The joint is made by caulking gasket inside the socket for about one third of its depth and then filling in the remainder of the socket with portland cement and sand mortar, and finishing with a smooth 45° fillet.

Fixing cast iron pipes Great care should be taken to see that pipes when fixed are in alignment or the stack will look very unsightly.

The fixing is carried out as follows:

(1). A chalk line is made be means of a chalked plumb line. The string is first chalked and then allowed to hang from the highest point over the centre of the drain collar. The string is then held taut and 'plucked', which leaves a chalk line down the centre where the stack will be fixed.
(2). The positions of the holes for the pipe nails are measured and marked on either side of the centre line.
(3). The holes are drilled and dry wood plugs driven into the wall.
(4). Commencing from the bottom, the pipes are now fixed to the wall by means of pipe nails driven into the wood plugs.

Cutting cast iron pipes The easiest method of cutting the pipes is by means of a chain wheel cutter, alternatively a hack saw may be used.

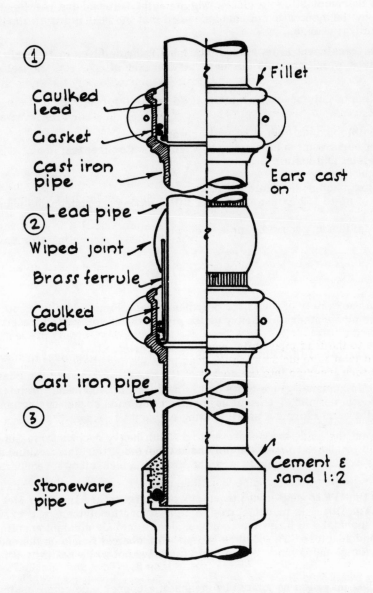

① Fillet

Caulked lead

Gasket

Cast iron pipe

Ears cast on

② Lead pipe

Wiped joint

Brass ferrule

Caulked lead

Cast iron pipe

③

Cement & sand 1:2

Stoneware pipe

JOINTS ON CAST IRON
SOIL, WASTE & VENT PIPES

Polythene Tubes I

Polyethylene or polythene is a thermoplastic produced by the polymerisation of ethylene. A thermoplastic is a plastic which can be softened and resoftened indefinitely by the application of heat, provided that the heat is insufficient to cause a chemical change.

Polythene is translucent in its natural state but is made black by the addition of carbon black, which protects the material from the effects of ultra violet light.

The properties of polythene which make it so suitable for service and distribution pipes are:

(a) Incorrodible and unaffected by soil or water;
(b) does not burst and the tube expands when the water freezes;
(c) easy to joint and instal;
(d) very light in weight:
(e) is non-toxic and non-contaminating;
(f) lengths of up to 152 m. can be obtained thus saving a considerable number of joints;
(g) may be laid underground by mole-ploughing.

JOINTING

There is a large variety of joints for polythene pipes, some joints being for normal gauge pipes, others for heavy gauge pipes, whilst some can be used for either.

Fig. 1 shows the 'Alkalite' joint manufactured by Imperial Chemical Industries Ltd.

The fitting is for normal gauge tubes and is made from 'Alkathene' brand polythene. A strip of nickel-chrome is moulded into each socket during manufacture, and this strip forms a small heating element.

To make a joint the leads are connected to a 6 volt heavy duty battery. Sufficient heat is produced to melt the polythene tube and fitting, thus making a homogeneous weld. Joints include straight couplings, tees, elbows, reducers and adaptors.

Fig. 2 shows the 'Platronga' joint manufactured by Yorkshire Imperial Metals Ltd, Leeds. The fitting is manufactured in high-strength polythene and is suitable for both normal and heavy gauge pipes. Joints include straight coupling tees, bends and adaptors. The joint is made with a conical flange on the end of the tube, the flange being made by a simple forming tool while heating with a blowlamp.

Polythene tubes may also be jointed by means of a copper pipe compression fitting, such as 'Kontite', and 'Conex', 'Instantor', Prestex', etc. With these fittings it is essential to use a copper insert and a copper fitting one size larger than the plastic pipe, i.e a 19 mm diameter plastic pipe would require a 25 mm copper fitting. Fig. 3 shows a joint using a 'Kontite' fitting.

Fig. 4 shows the 'Vulcathene Polyfusion' joint manufactured by J.S. and F. Folkard Ltd, Middlesex. The joint is suitable for both normal and heavy gauge pipes. The joint is made by a special tool which melts the mating surfaces which, when pressed together, fuse and form a welded joint.

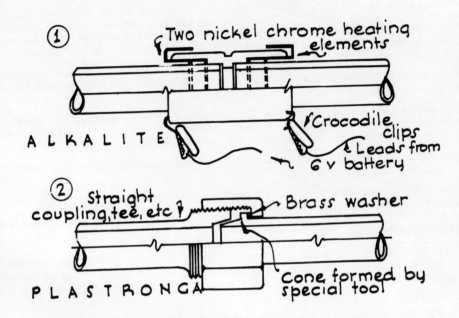

① Two nickel chrome heating elements

ALKALITE

Crocodile clips
& Leads from
6 v battery

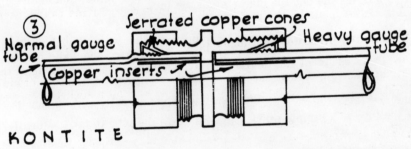

② Straight coupling, tee, etc ?

Brass washer

PLASTRONGA

Cone formed by special tool

③ Serrated copper cones

Normal gauge tube

Heavy gauge tube

Copper inserts

KONTITE

④ For socket

Special steel tool heated with blowlamp

Welded joint

For spigot

VULCATHENE POLYFUSION

POLYTHENE TUBES

Polythene Tubes II

FIXING (FIG. 1)

Wherever possible continuous support should be provided, alternatively the pipe may be fixed by use of standard metal pipe clips; clips made of rigid P.V.C. are obtainable.

To prevent undue sagging and to give a neat appearance, the clip spacing should be as follows:

Horizontal runs—up to 25 mm diameter 14 times the outside diameter of the tube between the centres of the support. Above 25 mm diameter 16 times the outside diameter of the tube between the centres of the support.

Vertical runs—for all sizes, 24 times the outside diameter of the tube between the centres of support.

To allow for expansion the clips should not be tightened so that they bite into the tube, and excessive tension on the tube before clipping should be avoided.

BENDING (FIG. 2)

Cold—tubes up to 51 mm diameter can be bent cold to a radius of not less than 8 times the outside diameter of the tube. Due to the elasticity of the tube, cold bends will tend to straighten out, and it is therefore necessary to clip close to a cold bend.

Hot—permanent bends can be made with the application of heat to a radius as small as 3 times the outside diameter of the tube. Bends on tubes up to 32 mm diameter can be made by use of a beading spring as follows:

Apply heat to the pipe by inserting the pipe in boiling water for about 5 minutes or by careful application of a blow lamp. The lamp should be turned down to its lowest level and the flame played gently on the full length of the bend for at least 3 minutes.

Insert the bending spring into the tube, and bend carefully with the hands.

Place the tube in a simple wooden jig and allow the tube to cool naturally, and release when cold.

The jig should be a little more acute than required for the bend, to allow for a slight tendency for the tube to straighten out in cooling.

For bends of 35 mm to 100 mm diameter, sand loading is necessary.

Plug one end of the tube and hold the tube in an upright position with the plug at the bottom.

Pour in cold sand to a point clear of where the bend will be started. The tube should be gently tapped with a dresser to consolidate the sand.

Pour in hot sand (at a temperature of approximately 100°C) for at least the length of the bend and tap again to consolidate the sand.

Complete the filling of the tube with cold sand and plug the open end.

When the tube becomes warm, bend slowly and carefully in a right angled support.

Place the tube in a jig and pour on cold water to hasten the cooling.

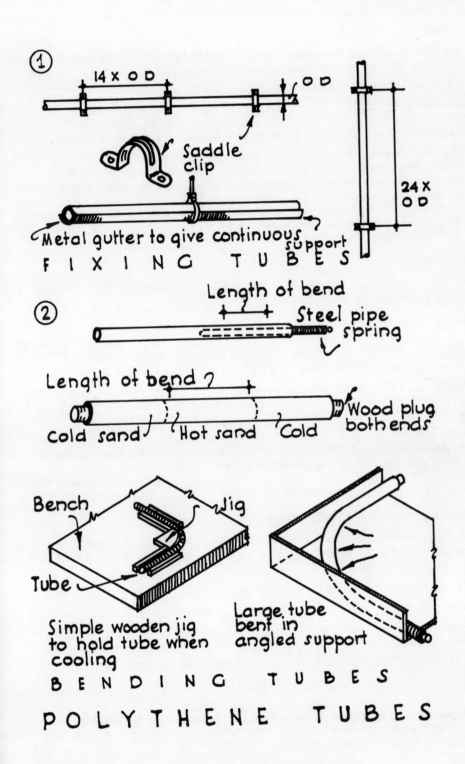

① 14 X O D   O D

Saddle clip

24 X O D

Metal gutter to give continuous support

FIXING TUBES

② Length of bend

Steel pipe spring

Length of bend?

cold sand   Hot sand   Cold

Wood plug both ends

Bench   Jig

Tube

Simple wooden jig to hold tube when cooling

Large tube bent in angled support

BENDING TUBES

POLYTHENE TUBES

Methods of Fixing Pipes

LEAD

To prevent sagging lead pipes require good support, and horizontal waste pipes carrying hot discharges require a continuous support.

Distance between supports

Up to and including	Horizontal runs	Vertical runs
38 mm diameter	610 mm apart	762 mm apart
51 mm diameter and over	762 mm apart	1·000 m to 1·2 mm

Types of support Pipes up to and including 38 mm diameter, Fig. 1: (a) wrought iron pipe hook with a lead protecting sheath between the pipe and the hook; (b) tinned steel saddle clip; (c) lead tacks soldered on to the pipe. Pipes 51 mm diameter and over, Fig. 2: (a) single or double lead tacks soldered or lead-burned on to the pipe; (b) cast lead socket soldered or leadburned to the pipe; (c) continuous support. Note Lead tacks may be either cast or made from 3.42 mm milled sheet lead.

COPPER

Clips or brackets should be made from either copper or brass; malleable iron clips should not be used because corrosion occurs between copper and iron.

Distances between supports (light gauge pipes C.P. 310)

Diameter in mm.	13	19	25	32	38	51	64	76	102
Horizontal runs (distance in m)	1·3	1·6	1·6	2·5	2·5	2·8	3·0	3·0	3·0
Vertical runs (distance in m)	1·8	2·5	2·5	3·0	3·0	3·0	3·7	3·7	3·7

Types of support Fig. 3 Copper (a) saddle clip; (b) double spacing clip; (c) single spacing clip; Brass (d) screw on wall bracket; (e) building in wall bracket (school board pattern); (f) building in single pipe ring bracket (a piece of steel pipe threaded at one end can be cut to any length for building into the wall).

MILD STEEL or WROUGHT IRON

For small diameter pipes fixed to timber, a galvanised steel saddle clip may be used. For pipes projecting from the wall, black or galvanised malleable iron brackets are used.

Distance between supports (Mild steel pipes C.P. 310)

Diameter mm.	13	19	25	32	38	51	64	76	102
Horizontal runs (distance in m)	1·8	2·5	2·5	2·8	3·0	3·0	3·7	3·7	3·7
Vertical runs (distance in m)	2·5	3·0	3·0	3·0	3·7	3·7	4·6	4·6	4·6

Types of support, Fig. 4 (a) screw on wall brackets; (b) building in wall brackets; (c) pipe hanger which can be made from a piece of wrought iron rod with clips made from sheet steel.

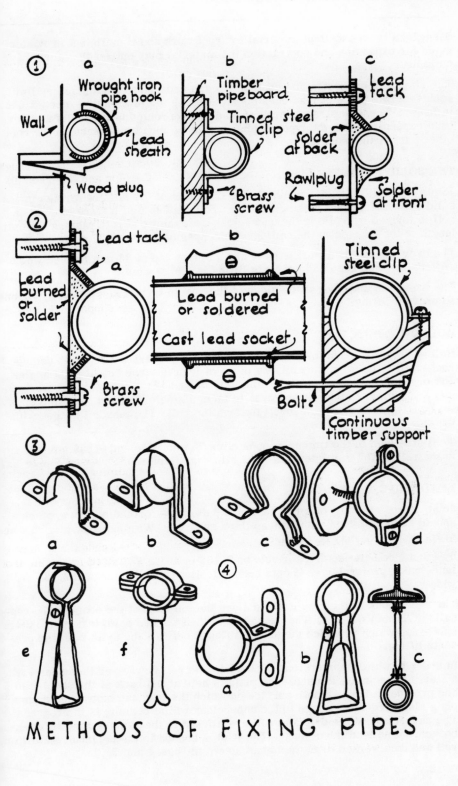

① **a** Wrought iron pipe hook · Wall · Lead sheath · Wood plug
b Timber pipe board · Tinned steel clip · Brass screw
c Lead tack · Solder at back · Rawlplug · Solder at front

② **a** Lead tack · Lead burned or solder · Brass screw
b Lead burned or soldered · Cast lead socket
c Tinned steel clip · Bolt · Continuous timber support

③ a   b   c   d

④ a   b   c   e   f

METHODS OF FIXING PIPES

Expansion joints in Sheet Lead

Sheet lead is an excellent material for roof work and if sufficient provision i made for expansion and contraction the material may outlast the fabric of the building.

The effects of expansion and contraction are reduced to a satisfactory limit i each separate piece of lead does not exceed 2.3 m² in area or exceed 3.048 in length. These separate pieces of lead are connected by means of a water-tight expansion joint, the type of joint depending upon its position on the roof other part of the building.

THE SOLID ROLL, Fig. 1

Joints on lead flat roofs running in the direction of the fall are formed by solid rolls. The usual distance between rolls is 685 mm (centre to centre). T roll is formed by working the undercloak over the wood roll, rasping the enti length of the edge down the nailing with copper nails every 76 mm.

The overcloak is then worked over and a splash lap of 38 mm formed which stiffens the free edge and prevents lifting in a high wind.

The timber is underset at the sides of the roll to form a key for the lead, and so prevent lifting.

HOLLOW ROLLS, Fig. 2

Hollow rolls are used for pitched roofs where they are not liable to damage t roof traffic. To form the roll, one piece of lead is turned up at right angles 102 mm high. Another piece is similarly turned 121 mm high. The overlappi piece of 19 mm is then turned over to form a single welt and the two pieces c lead curled over a wood mandril to form the roll. The mandril is then with-drawn.

To fix the lead to the timber, copper clips 76 mm wide and 0.559 mm are fitt in the roll at 762 mm intervals. The clips are fixed to the roof by copper nai

LEAD DRIPS, Fig. 3

Joints across the fall of a flat roof or a gutter are formed by drips, which should be 38 mm high with anticapillary grooves. With drips 50 mm high an over, the groove may be omitted.

The distance between drips should be 2.133 m and 2.743 m, the 2.133 m dis-tance being preferable as it cuts economically from the standard 2.438 m wide roll.

The undercloak of the drip is fixed along the top edge of the boarding by copp nails at 76 mm centres. The overcloak is then worked down leaving a 38 mm splash lap which provides the same stiffened edge as the solid roll, and pre-vents lifting.

In order to work the overcloak of the drip and roll down over the undercloak, a steel driving plate is used. The plate is held at the back of the sheet lead and provides a hard smooth surface on which the lead can be worked down. T plate also prevents damage to the undercloak whilst bossing is in progress. The undercloak of the drip and roll are worked in the same way as an externa corner, but no lead is cut away. The lead is bossed to the height of the drip o roll and then worked over the top as shown in Figs. 1 and 3.

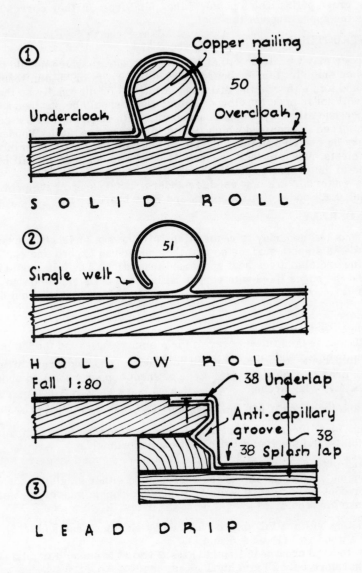

① Copper nailing

50

Undercloak   Overcloak

S O L I D   R O L L

② 51

Single welt

H O L L O W   R O L L

Fall 1:80   38 Underlap

Anti-capillary
groove   38

38 Splash lap

③

L E A D   D R I P

E X P A N S I O N   J O I N T S
I N   S H E E T   L E A D

Sheet Copper Roof Work I

Sheet copper is an excellent material for roofing purposes; it is light in wei
very durable, and free from 'creep'. After a time sheet copper becomes co:
by a pale green patina which protects the metal from further corrosion and
enhances the appearance of the roof.

UNDERSTRUCTURE

Sheet copper may be laid on either timber or concrete which should be solid
and finished smooth. Timber boards should be 19 mm or 25 mm tongued an
grooved and laid either in the direction of the fall or diagonally so that any
warping will not impede the flow of water. Nails should be punched well bel
the surface, and all sharp edges rounded off. With concrete roofs a cement
and sand screed is required which is laid to the required fall. Wooden fixing
blocks may be inserted in the concrete to faciliate the fixing down of the cop
per with cleats. When breeze concrete is used, two coats of asphalt paint mu
be applied to the breeze to protect the copper from corrosion.
Many new materials are now used for understructures, and have proved very
successful, e.g. woodwool slabs, block and fibre boards.

FELT UNDERLAY

An inodorous felt underlay is required for all types of understructures. The
felt provides a smooth surface so that the copper can expand and contract wi
out wearing and also gives heat and sound insulation. The felt should be butt
jointed and the edges fixed with copper nails. Iron nails should on no accoun
be used as electrolytic action may be set up resulting in the corrosion of the
copper.

TYPE OF SHEET COPPER

Setting out
In order to provide for expansion and contraction, and to prevent lifting, the
maximum area of each individual piece of sheet copper when laid should not
exceed the following areas:

up to and including 0.559 mm — 1.300 m²; 0.457 mm — 1.114 m²

These individual pieces of sheet-copper are jointed together by means of ex
pansion joints, and the roof must be set out accordingly.

Expansion Joints
Joints running across the fall of the roof may be either single lock cross we:
(Fig. 1), or double lock cross welts (Fig. 2). The double lock cross welt is
essential for flat roofs.

Joints running with the fall may be formed by standing seams (Fig. 3), or by
means of a wood roll (Figs. 4, 5, and 6).
The round top and ornamental rolls (Figs. 7 and 8) are used for pitched roofs
and are therefore only 25 mm high.
For roofs likely to carry pedestrian traffic the roll is used as the standing
seam may be trodden down and cause water to penetrate through the single
lock welt.

Method of fixing
In order to fix the sheet copper to the roof copper, cleats a:
inserted in the rolls, welts or standing seams. These cleats are 0.559 mm
copper 51 mm wide, and spaced at from 304 mm to 460 mm centres (Fig. 9).
timber roofs the cleats are nailed to the timber with at least two copper nail
32 mm long. On concrete roofs the cleats are fishtailed and set in the concr:
where required.

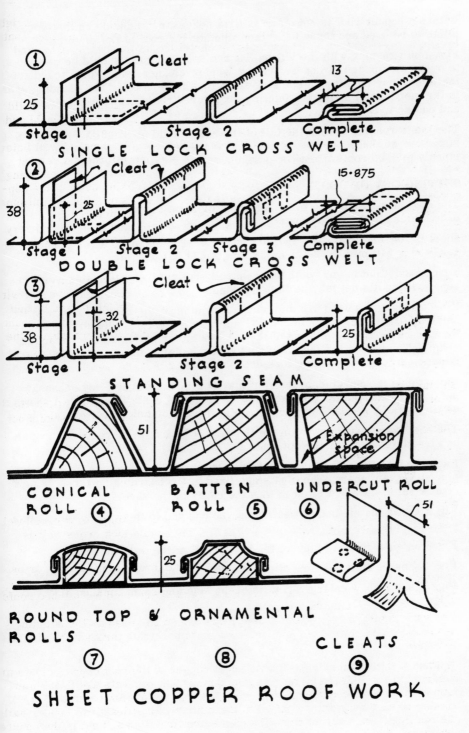

① **SINGLE LOCK CROSS WELT**

25 — Stage 1 — Cleat — Stage 2 — 13 — Complete

② **DOUBLE LOCK CROSS WELT**

38 — 25 — Cleat — Stage 1 — Stage 2 — Stage 3 — 15·875 — Complete

③ **STANDING SEAM**

38 — 32 — Cleat — Stage 1 — Stage 2 — 25 — Complete

51 — Expansion space

CONICAL ROLL ④ — **BATTEN ROLL** ⑤ — **UNDERCUT ROLL** ⑥

51

25

ROUND TOP & ORNAMENTAL ROLLS ⑦ ⑧ — **CLEATS** ⑨

SHEET COPPER ROOF WORK

Sheet Copper Roof Work II

Before a copper roof is set out it is first necessary to decide on the types of joints to be used and these depend on whether the roof is flat or pitched.

For joints running with the fall on flat roofs, batten rolls should be used so as to prevent damage by roof traffic, e.g. window cleaners etc. For pitched roofs the joints may be either a standing seam or a battern roll. The standing seam is the more usual method of jointing for pitched roofs because it is cheaper and easier to fix.

The joints running across the fall of the roof should be double lock cross welt staggered so that no two welts coincide at the roll or standing seam. For steeply pitched roofs it may be possible to use single lock welts.

SETTING OUT OF ROOFS

The roof may be covered by either sheet or strip copper, 0.711, 0.610 or 0.559 thick. (dead soft temper).

Sheet is flat material over 460 mm in width. The standard sizes of sheets are 1.219 m × 610 mm, 1.829 m × 914 mm, 2.438 × 1.219 m.

Strip is supplied in any width and generally not cut to length. It is usually supplied in coils but may be flat or folded.

If sheet copper is used 610 mm wide, the widths of the bays for batten rolls and standing seams are 551 mm and 539 mm respectively. These distances give the allowance for the jointing of the bays by either batten rolls or standing seams. To keep within the stipulated maximum area for each bay the maximum distance between the double lock cross welts is 2 m.

Using these measurements the roof may now be set out, it being necessary to set out the centre lines for the joints by means of chalk lines. Fig. 1 shows the setting out of both flat and pitched roofs with the distances between the bays.

The sheets against the wall on the flat roof will have to be reduced in width and length to allow for the upstand.

Each sheet is fixed to the roof boarding by sheet copper cleats 51 mm wide placed 381 mm apart. The cleats are fixed to the boarding by three 38 mm copper nails, and are welted in with the edges of the sheets.

Fig. 2 shows the method of weathering the upstand to the wall by means of a cover flashing.

Fig. 3 shows a finished view of the batten roll at the wall and gutter.

Fig. 4 shows a finished view of the standing seam at the ridge and gutter.

Figs. 5 and 6 show enlarged details of the standing seam finished at eaves and ridge respectively.

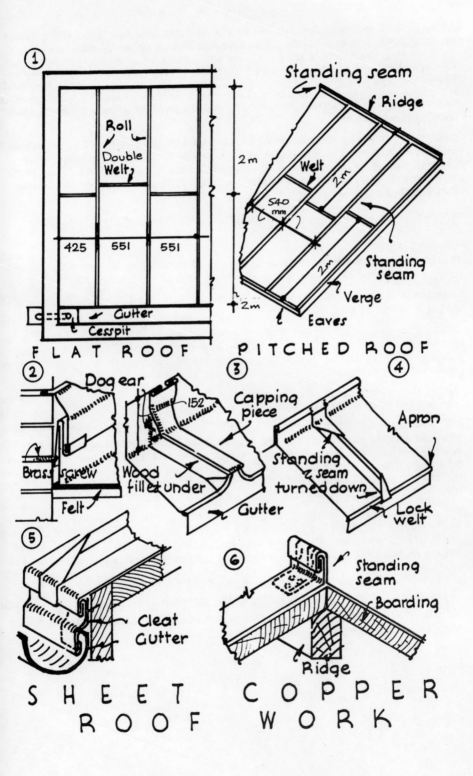

① **FLAT ROOF**

Roll
Double Welt
425   551   551
Gutter
Cesspit

PITCHED ROOF

Standing seam
Ridge
Welt
2 m
540 mm
2 m
Standing seam
Verge
Eaves
2 m
2 m

② Dog ear
Brass screw
Felt

③ 152
Capping piece
Wood fillet under
Gutter

④ Apron
Standing seam turned down
Lock welt

⑤ Cleat
Gutter

⑥ Standing seam
Boarding
Ridge

SHEET COPPER ROOF WORK

Raking Flashing and Soakers

The method of weathering a pitched roof at the intersection of a wall or chimney stack, is known as flashing. The type of flashing depends upon the type of roof covering. For plain tiles or slates, soakers and continuous strip flashing are normally used, but for contoured tiles and corrugated asbestos cement sheets, soakers are dispensed with and overflashing is used.

Soakers (Fig. 1) The first operation in flashing to plain tiling or slating is the fixing of the soakers.

Soakers are made by the plumber, but are fixed by the roofer as he is laying his slates or tiles. The width of a soaker is 178 mm minimum; this allows a 76 mm turnup to the wall, and 102 mm under the tiles or slates. The length the soaker is determined by the length and lap of the tiles or slates and may be calculated as follows:

$$\text{Gauge} + \text{lap} + 25 \text{ mm} = \frac{\text{Length of slate or tile} - \text{lap}}{2} + \text{lap} + 25 \text{ mm}$$

The 25 mm allowance is for turning the top of the soaker 25 mm over the top edge of the tile or slate, thus preventing the soaker from slipping.

Example Calculate the size of a soaker required for a 508 × 254 mm slate, having a lap of 76 mm.

$$\text{Length of soaker} = \left(\frac{508 \text{ mm} - 76 \text{ mm}}{2}\right) + 76 \text{ mm} + 25 \text{ mm}$$
$$= 216 + 76 + 25$$
$$= 317 \text{ mm}$$

<u>Answer</u> size of soaker = 317 mm × 178 mm

Fig. 2 shows the method of setting out the flashing. A strip of lead 165 mm-191 mm wide is placed against the brickwork, 13 mm above the line of the slates or tiles. The lines of the brick joints are then marked across the lead by a chalkline, and the rake of the flashing marked where these lines intersect the waterline. An allowance of 25 mm-38 mm is made for the turn into the brick joint and the triangular portion is cut away and used for lead wedges.

Fig. 3 shows how the flashing is fixed to the brickwork by lead wedges, two wedges being required for each step of the flashing. The free edge of the flashing is prevented from lifting by a lead tack 51 mm wide fixed at intervals of 762 mm. After the leadwork is completed the brick joint is pointed up by the bricklayer. Mastic is better than cement and sand for this purpose as it does not crack with expansion and contraction of the lead.

Fig. 4 shows the type of flashing used for contour tiling or corrugated asbestos cement sheets. Soakers are not required and the weathering is simply an overflashing dressed over the first corrugation.

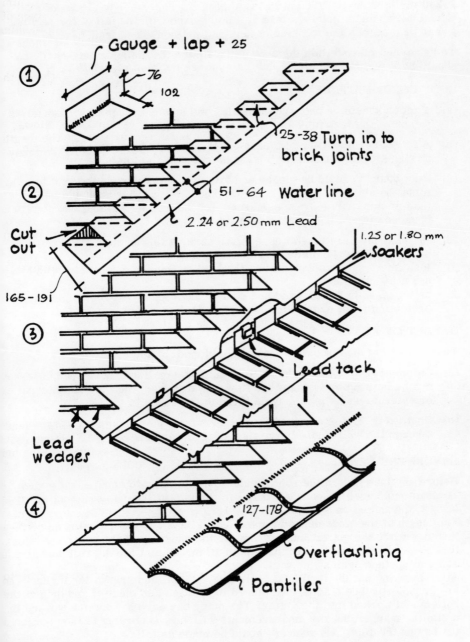

① Gauge + lap + 25

76

102

25-38 Turn in to brick joints

② 51-64 Water line

2.24 or 2.50 mm Lead

1.25 or 1.80 mm Soakers

Cut out

165-191

③ Lead tack

Lead wedges

④ 127-178

Overflashing

Pantiles

R A K I N G   F L A S H I N G S
A N D   S O A K E R S

Lead Flat

A lead flat should be designed so that each single piece of lead does not exceed 2.230 m^2 in area or 3.000 m in length, Fig. 1. These single pieces of lead are joined by expansion joints, a lead roll being used with the fall of the roof and a lead drip across the fall (see expansion joints on sheet-lead, page 27).

To keep each piece within the above size limits, the distance between drips should be 2.000 m − 2.400 m and the distance between rolls 675 mm.

ROOF CONSTRUCTION

(a) Timber should be properly seasoned and strong enough to withstand the weight of the lead plus any snow or roof traffic.

(b) A fall of not less than 38 mm in 3.048 m should be obtained by placing firring pieces of different thickness on top of the joists.

(c) Roof boards should be planed and laid diagonally across the roof to minimise the effect of warping. The thickness of the boards should be not less than 25 mm, the nail heads punched well below the surface, sharp corners rounded off, and high places planed down.

(d) An underlay of bitumen impregnated sarking felt or stout waterproof building paper should be provided as this gives:
1. less frictional resistance when the lead expands and contracts with temperature changes;
2. an increase in the thermal and sound insulation of the roof;
3. protection from metal corrosion when laid on a concrete roof.

OUTLET OF FLAT

There are two types of outlets, (a) catch pit, and (b) chute.

(a) Catch pit—Fig. 2. With this type of outlet a small pressure head of water can be built up to increase the flow of water from the flat. An internal or external outlet pipe may be fitted to the cesspit.

(b) Chute—Fig. 3. A chute is normally an extension of the gutter carried through the wall to discharge into a rainwater head.

LAYING THE LEAD

Before any lead is laid the roof should be swept down to ensure that no debris is left to puncture the lead. After the gutter is laid, bay number 1 is laid, then bays 2, 3, 4 and so on, as shown in Fig. 1.

The length of the piece of lead for bay 1 will be 2.360 m. This allows a 127 mm turn down into the gutter and 102 mm for the underlap of the drip. The width this piece of lead will be 914 mm which allows 89 mm for the roll underlap and 152 mm upstand against the wall.

After marking out the lead by a chalk line, the roll and drip at the highest end are bossed up. The lead is then placed in position and the roll and drip at the bottom end worked into the gutter. The other bays are set out and worked in a similar manner, but the measurements will vary according to the position of the bay on the roof. Allowances should be made as follows:

roll overcloak—165 mm   roll undercloak—89 mm
drip overcloak—102 mm   drip undercloak—102 mm
upstand to wall—152 mm

To complete the work a lead cover flashing is fixed over the upstand as shown in Fig. 1.

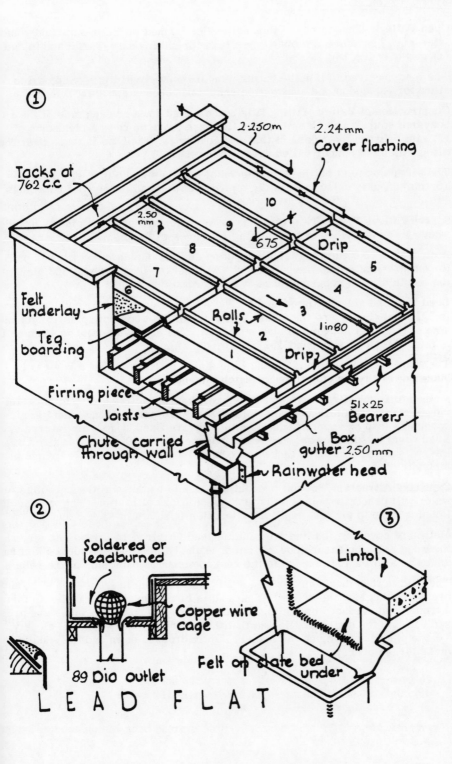

①
2.250m 2.24mm
Cover flashing

Tacks at 762 c.c

2.50 mm

10

9

8   675   Drip

7   5

Felt underlay
6   4

Teg boarding   Rolls   3   1in80

2   Drip

1

Firring piece   51x25

Joists   Bearers

Chute carried through wall   Box gutter 2.50 mm

Rainwater head

②
Soldered or leadburned

Lintol ③

Copper wire cage

89 Dio outlet   Felt or slate bed under

L E A D   F L A T

Lead Valleys, Hips and Ridges

Open Valleys These are the internal angles formed where two pitched roofs intersect. There are two open types, (a) with gutter board, Fig. 1, and (b) without gutter board, Fig. 2.

The lead required to line the gutter is approximately 610 mm wide, and to allow for expansion and contraction should not exceed 3.000 m in length

Construction of Valley Tilting fillets are nailed down on each side of the roof boarding so that, when the slates or tiles are fixed, there is a clearance of 127 mm between the raking of the roof coverings. The lead is taken over the tilting fillet and copper bailed every 152 mm.

The expansion joint between the pieces of lead is simply a lap of 102 mm-152 mm. The lap also fastens the top edge of the lead to the roof boardings, Fig. 3.

Secret Valleys Fig. 4 This valley is neater than the open types but is not ideal where trees are close to the building as leaves will soon choke the gutter.

A clearance of 25 mm between the raking edge of the slates or tiles is sufficient for entry of water into the gutter. The width of the lead is about 508 mm, and the length of each separate piece 2.134 m maximum.

Lead hips and ridges, Figs. 5 and 6 The length of each separate piece of lead is 2.134 maximum, and the width is the size of the wood roll, plus 152 on each side of the roll to cover the slates or tiles. The expansion joint is a lap of 1 mm for the ridge, and about 152 mm for the hip.

The wood roll should stand clear of the slates or tiles so that a key can be obtained for the lead which will help to prevent lifting.

Method of fixing Great care must be exercised when fixing lead to hips and ridges otherwise there is danger of the lead lifting in a strong wind. For ridge coverings lead or copper tacks 51 mm wide are fixed at 762 mm intervals. Lead coverings to hips require lead or copper tacks 102 mm wide fixed at intervals of 610 mm. The tacks are copper nailed to the top of the ridge or hip rafter before the wood rolls are fixed.

Capillary Attraction Special precautions should be taken at the lap joints or water will penetrate between the lead by capillary attraction. The method of forming a lap to prevent capillary attraction is shown in Figs. 3 and 6.

Method of covering To find the width of lead required, the amount to cover the wood roll is measured by a strip of lead. To this measurement 305 mm added, to allow a 152 mm lap to the roof covering on each side of the roll.

The lead is then marked out with a chalk line 152 mm in from each side, and a crease made along these lines. The lead is turned up at right angles to form a trough and is placed on the top of the ridge or hip roll. The sides are pressed down on the slates or tiles so that the centre fits the wood roll closely. To complete the covering the lead is lightly dressed down and the ends of the tacks turned over.

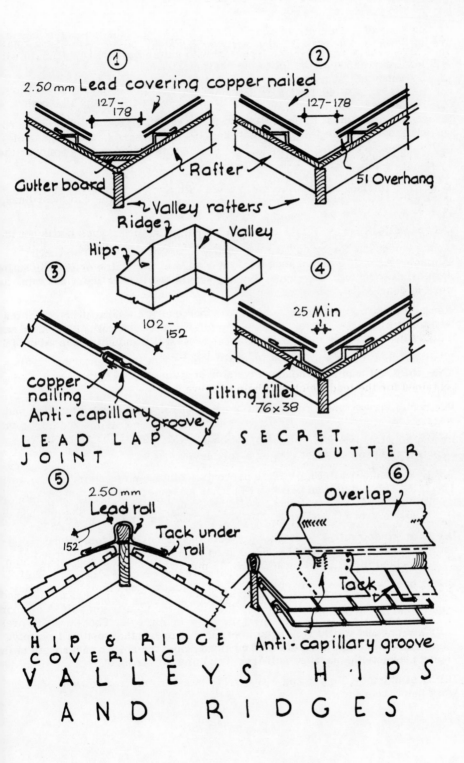

① 2.50 mm Lead covering copper nailed

127 – 178

Gutter board

Rafter

51 Overhang

Valley rafters

② 127 – 178

Ridge

Hips

Valley

③ 102 – 152

copper nailing

Anti - capillary groove

L E A D   L A P
J O I N T

④ 25 Min

Tilting fillet
76 × 38

S E C R E T
G U T T E R

⑤ 2.50 mm
Lead roll

Tack under roll

152

H I P & R I D G E
C O V E R I N G

⑥ Overlap

Tack

Anti - capillary groove

V A L L E Y S   H I P S

A N D   R I D G E S

Copper and Lead Damp-proof Courses

The purpose of a damp-proof course (D.P.C) is to stop the movement of moi
ure up, down or sideways through a porous material.

A D.P.C. must possess the following characteristics:
(a) be dense and impervious;
(b) be resistant to corrosion or deterioration;
(c) adhere strongly to mortar;
(d) permit movement in the wall without fracturing or tearing;
(e) be easy to handle and manipulate.

Sheet lead or copper have all these properties and are therefore excellent
materials for D.P.Cs.

Lead The thickness of lead in mm varies with the position of the D.P.C. and
the type of work. For cheaper work 1.25 mm lead may be used whilst for be
class work, 1.80, 2.24 or even 2.50 mm lead may be used.

Protection. It is important to protect lead from corrosion when in contact wi
fresh cement mortar by coating with heavy bituminous paint. The coating
should be applied to the underside of the lead before being laid, and to the up
surface after laying. This upper coating should be allowed to dry before furt
work is done.

Joints. An expansion joint should be provided every 3.048 m. The joint may
be a simple lap of 102 mm or a double welt, Fig. 1 (a), (b). Welts are used wh
a slight head of water may exist e.g. in parapet walls and chimney stacks.

Lead does not cause staining of the wall, which is an important consideration
when D.P.Cs are placed in expensive stone buildings.

Copper The thickness of copper used varies with type of work. 0.315 or
0.254 mm may be used for cheaper work and 0.559 mm thick for high class
work.

Protection. Copper is not attacked by cement mortar and it is therefore unnecessary to protect sheet copper before laying.

D.P.C. at base of wall, Fig. 1 This prevents moisture from rising up the wall
The D.P.C. should be laid between the inner and outer 114.700 mm leaves, on
top of the sleeper wall and underneath the timber wall plate. The height of th
D.P.C. above ground level should be at least 152 mm and not more than 305 m

D.P.C. at window sill, Fig. 2 This protects the timber sill from rising moisture. It should be extended 114.700 mm on either side of the sill, turned up
25 mm behind the sill and turned down 25 mm over the brickwork at the front

D.P.C. over window or door opening, Fig. 3 This prevents moisture passing
downwards to the concrete lintel. The D.P.C. should be extended 152.4 mm o
either side of the opening.

D.P.C. at parapet wall, Fig. 4 The lower D.P.C. prevents moisture from pass
ing downwards to the concrete or timber roof, and the D.P.C. underneath the
coping prevents the parapet wall from becoming wet from above.

D.P.C. at chimney, Figs. 5 and 6 Prevents moisture moving down to brickwork below roof level.

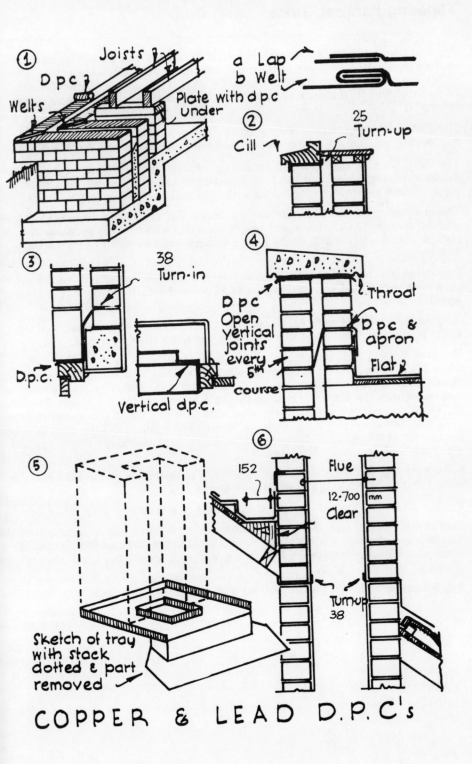

① Joists

D p c

Welts

Plate with d p c under

a Lap
b Welt

② Cill
25
Turn-up

③
38
Turn-in

D.P.C.

Vertical d.p.c.

④
Throat

D p c
Open vertical joints every 5ᵗʰ course

D p c & apron

Flat

⑤

Sketch of tray with stack dotted & part removed

⑥
152

Flue

12·700 mm
Clear

Turn-up
38

COPPER & LEAD D.P.C's

Tapering Parapet Gutter

For buildings of over two storeys in height a parapet wall gutter is preferable to the eaves gutter, because of the ease and safety with which the gutter may be either cleaned or repaired. The parapet wall gutter may also be preferred. from an architectural point of view, and used on buildings of even one storey in height.

The gutter-framing is constructed by the carpenter but the plumber should co-operate with the carpenter in deciding the positions of the drips, rolls etc.

The rule that no single piece of sheet lead shall exceed 2.230 m² in area nor 3.000 m in length should be strictly adhered to when setting out the gutter, and a plan, drawn to scale, will determine the positions of the expansion joints.

The minimum width of the gutter at the lowest end is 229 mm to provide access without damage to the slates or tiles. This width will steadily increase to the highest end due to the fall of the gutter which should be not less than 38 mm in 3.000 m.

Due to the widening of the gutter to the highest end, the upper part of the gutter may have to be lined with two pieces of sheet lead joined together by means of a roll.

Alternatively on long gutters, an outlet may be provided at both ends and the sheet lead at the centre and highest point joined together by a roll.

Gutter outlets The simplest method of forming an outlet to the gutter is by means of a chute passing through the parapet wall and discharging into a hopper head. Alternatively a 229 × 229 × 152 mm lead cesspit may be used which dispenses with the unsightly hole in the wall necessary for the chute. The cesspit also provides a small pressure head of water which increases the rate of flow in the rainwater down pipe. A 76 mm or 89 mm dia outlet pipe is fitted to base of the cesspit which passes through the parapet wall to discharge into a hopper head.

Setting out the gutter A line diagram of the cross section of the gutter at the lowest end is drawn to a large scale as shown in Fig. 1.

To draw the plan, the total length of the gutter is drawn to a smaller scale.

The 229 mm × 229 mm cesspit is then drawn on the plan and the gutter divided with drips at distances between 2.743 m and 2.134 m. The widths across the drips may now be transferred from the cross section, and the complete plan drawn as shown in Fig. 2

Fig. 3 is a section through the parapet wall and gutter.

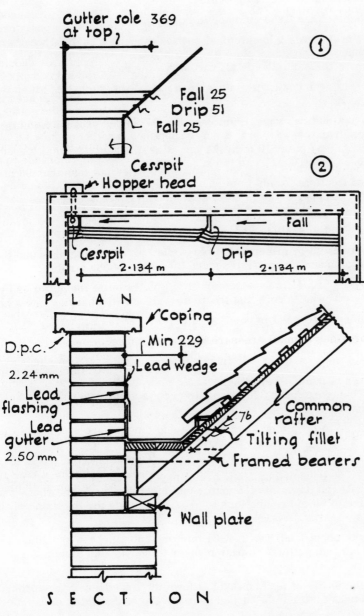

Gutter sole 369 at top

① Fall 25
Drip 51
Fall 25

Cesspit
Hopper head

② Fall

Cesspit
2.134 m
Drip
2.134 m

PLAN

Coping
Min 229
D.p.c.
Lead wedge
2.24 mm
Lead flashing
76
Common rafter
Lead gutter
2.50 mm
Tilting fillet
Framed bearers

Wall plate

SECTION

TAPERING PARAPET
GUTTER

Weathering of Skylights

A skylight is a sash fixed on a pitched roof to provide natural lighting and, if necessary, ventilation to the room below.

The sash may be either fixed or made to open.

Weathering Fig. 1 shows a longitudinal section through a skylight weathered with either sheet or copper or aluminium. Since the application of these two metals is almost the same the detail will serve for both.

Sheet copper has been dealt with in previous pages, and the use of aluminium is now described.

The metal is available as super-purity quality 99. 99 per cent pure and in this condition it is soft and easy to work. It may be obtained in rolls weighing 12. 7 kg 152 mm, 305 mm, 457 mm, 610 mm, 914 mm wide, the gauge normally used for roofing purposes being 0. 914 mm thick.

The nails used for fixing aluminium should be aluminium alloy, zinc or heavily galvanised steel; copper or plain steel nails should never be used because of corrosion of the aluminium by electrolytic action.

The weathering to the skylight should be carried out in the following manner:

The apron is made up by either welded or welted joints and fixed in position; cleats are fixed under the apron to secure the lower edge.

Soakers are fixed between the slates or tiles, and these may be fixed by the slater or tiler when he is covering the roof.

The side flashings are fixed in position to cover over the soakers.

A continuous cleat is nailed to the top edge of the lining.

The top edge of the apron and side flashings are welted to the continuous cleat.

The back gutter is made up by either welded or welted joints and fixed in position, one side being extended 229 mm up the roof and the other side welted to the continuous cleat.

The sash is fixed to the lining and the sides and top rail are weathered with a sheathing.

A condensation gutter may be required if, for instance, the room below is a kitchen or is to be occupied by a number of people. Vapour condensing to water on the glass will run down into the gutter and discharge on to the roof. The gutter will have to be in two sections to provide a space for the fixing of the opening gear.

Weathering with sheet lead, Fig. 2 2.24 mm or 2. 50 mm lead should be used and the work carried out in a similar manner to copper and aluminium weathering.

The greater flexibility of lead however, allows the top edges of the apron, side flashings and back gutter to be turned over the top of the lining in one piece a shown.

The lower edge of the apron should be secured with lead tacks 51 mm wide at 762 mm centres.

The apron and backgutter may be bossed or leadburned. For small skylights the side flashings may be formed with one piece of sheet lead, but with larger skylights separate pieces may be required, welted together.

43

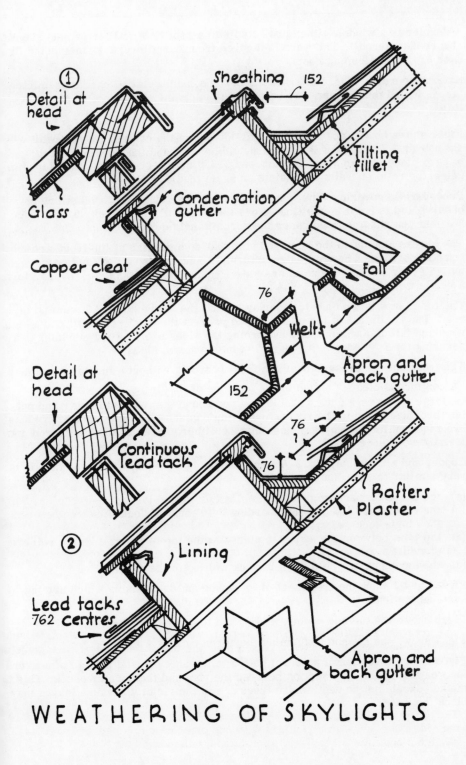

① Detail at head

Sheathing   152

Glass

Copper cleat

Condensation gutter

Tilting fillet

Fall

76

Welts

152

Apron and back gutter

Detail at head

Continuous lead tack

76

76

76

Rafters
Plaster

②

Lining

Lead tacks
762 centres

Apron and back gutter

WEATHERING OF SKYLIGHTS

Covering of Dormer Windows

A dormer is a window either projected into a roof (internal) or projected out of a roof (external). The word is derived from dormitory, a dormer being first used to light a sleeping room.

External dormer There are various designs, having flat, pitched or semicircular roofs and the dormer may be fixed in the centre of the roof or at eaves level.

Fig. 1 shows how to cover an external dormer in the centre of a roof with sheet lead. 2. 24, 2. 50 or 3. 15 mm should be used and the maximum area of each piece of lead should not exceed 2. 230 m², these pieces being joined together by rolls or welts (see joints on sheet lead).

Procedure in covering The front apron is formed by either leadburning or bossing, and is fixed in position before the wood sill. Lead tacks 51 mm wide at 762 mm centres are fixed under the apron to hold down the front edge, Fig. 4.

The cheeks are cut to the required size and, commencing at the front, are fixed in position. The front edge is turned round the front post and copper nailed every 5 mm. The nails are hidden by turning the lead back over to form a single welt, Fig. 5.

The top is now laid on a felt underlay so that the lead extends 229 mm up the roof. The treatment of the edges should prevent the lead from lifting in a high wind and this is accomplished by turning the sides over a wood moulding and securing the free edge by tacks at 762 mm centres, Fig. 3.

The front may be dressed over the front boarding without a moulding and may be laid down by lead tacks.

On large dormers, a gutter should be fixed round the front and sides, and outlets provided close to the roof intersection on each side. Intermediate fixings are required for the cheeks; these may be either secret tacks or soldered dots (see fixing of sheet lead).

Copper and aluminium, Fig. 2 The procedure of covering with these metals is very similar to sheet lead, except that:

(a) the apron is made up by either welded or welted joints;
(b) the cheeks are fixed to the boarding by means of cleats inserted between the single lock welts;
(c) the joint between the separate pieces at the top is either a batten roll or standing seam;
(d) the top edges are held down by lock welting to the cheeks.

Figs. 4 and 5 show the treatment of the apron and front fixing which are the same as for lead.

Fig. 6 shows the method of lock welting the top with the cheek.

Fig. 7 shows the method of forming the apron by lock welts.

Fig. 8 shows a section of a secret gutter which may be used instead of soakers for weathering the intersection between the roof and the dormer cheek. This method should not be used where trees are in the vicinity because leaves may block the gutter.

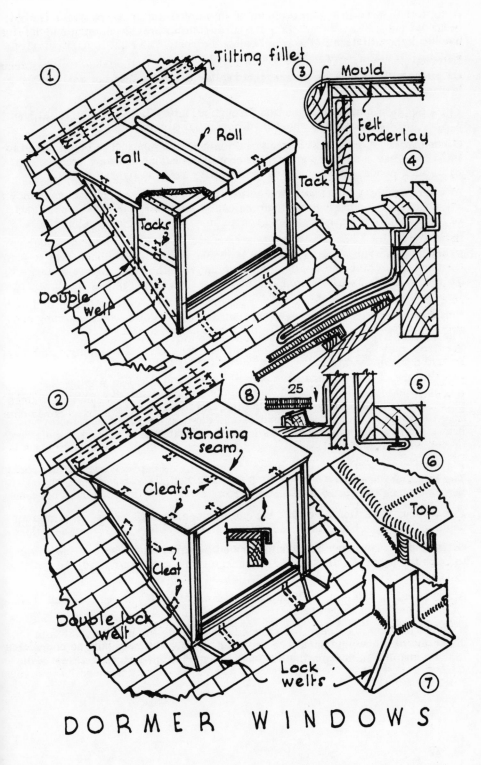

DORMER WINDOWS

Lantern Lights and Box Gutters

A lantern light is an improved form of skylight and may be fixed on a flat roof or at the ridge of a pitched roof. Its purpose is to provide lighting and, if necessary, ventilation to the room below the roof. The light is particularly suitable for fixing over sanitary apartments.

On plan, the light may be square, rectangular or in the shape of a polygon, e.g. hexagonal.

Fig. 1 shows a longitudinal section through a lantern light fixed on a flat roof. The weathering may be in sheet lead, copper or aluminium.

Condensation A good deal of condensation will take place if the light is to be fixed over, say, a sanitary apartment containing basins, showers etc. To deal with this a condensation gutter is formed all round the light, Fig. 2.

At intervals along the base of the gutter, 13 mm diameter condensation pipes are connected and carried through the curb to discharge the water on to the roof. Alternatively condensation grooves may be cut in the curb and the lead dressed in.

Procedure in weathering The apron is placed on the top of the curb to line the condensation gutter and weather the upstand from the roof. Cleats or tacks 51 mm wide are used to hold down the lower edge. The top edge is turned over the front of the gutter and nailed every 51 mm.

Condensation pipes are connected to the base of the gutter.

The light is fixed in position on the top of the curb.

The hips and ridge are covered as shown in Fig. 3.

Box Gutters These gutters have parallel sides and they are used on flat or pitched roofs. The box gutter does not take up as much roof space as the tapering gutter, which widens towards the top, and for this reason it is very suitable for roofs having skylights that extend down to the gutter, e.g. factory or drawing office roofs etc. The gutter may be situated between two sloping roofs or behind a parapet wall.

Fig. 4 shows a section through a box gutter situated between two sloping roofs. The minimum depth and width are 76 mm and 229 mm respectively. Drips are inserted along the gutter 2. 286 m apart.

Fig. 5 shows a section through a box gutter used for a flat roof, the minimum depth in this case being 152 mm, but the minimum width is 229 mm as before.

Gutter outlet This may be a chute, formed by carrying the sole of the gutter through the parapet wall so as to discharge into a rainwater head. An outlet is required for approximately every 15 m of gutter.

Alternatively a 229 mm × 229 mm × 152 mm catch pit may be inserted at the end or in the centre of the gutter.

If the outlet from the cesspit is carried down inside the building a 38 mm diameter overflow pipe should be provided. The overflow should be connected to the cesspit 76 mm from the base and be carried through the parapet wall.

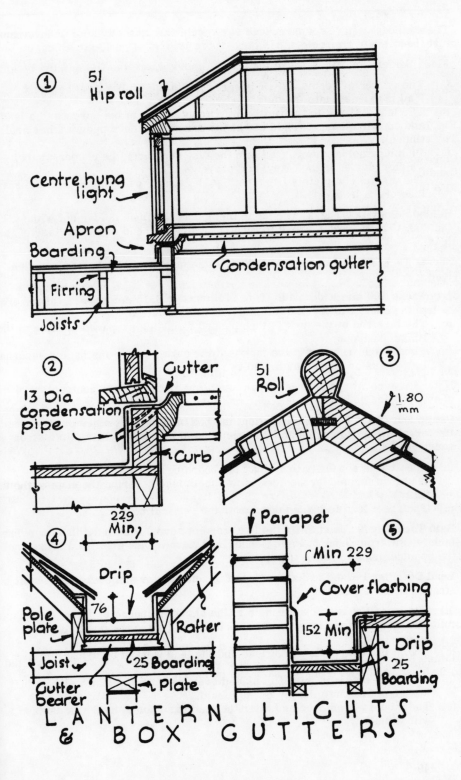

① 51 Hip roll

Centre hung light

Apron Boarding

Condensation gutter

Firring

Joists

② Gutter

13 Dia Condensation pipe

Curb

③ 51 Roll

1.80 mm

229 Min

④ Drip

76

Pole plate

Rafter

Joist

25 Boarding

Gutter bearer

Plate

⑤ Parapet

Min 229

Cover flashing

152 Min

Drip

25 Boarding

LANTERN LIGHTS & BOX GUTTERS

Fixing Sheet Lead

The methods used to fix sheet lead vary according to the type of understructure, i.e. timber, concrete, stone etc.

Flush Solder Dot, Fig. 1 Used for fixing timber where the fixing must be hide

(a) The carpenter forms a dish 10 mm deep in the timber and the sheet lead is dressed into the dish.
(b) The lead is fixed to the timber by a countersunk brass screw and a lead and copper washer. (The head of the screw and the copper washer are tinned).
(c) Plumbing solder is pressed into the dish and under the copper washer which provides a good 'key' and prevents lifting.
(d) The dish is completely filled with solder and is wiped flush with the surface of the lead.

Raised Solder Dot, Fig. 2 The same method as the flush solder dot without the dish. The solder is wiped to form a mushroom head on the surface of the lead.

Secret Tack, Fig. 3 As the name implies the tack is hidden behind the sheet lead.

(a) Tacks 100 mm wide made from 2.50 mm or 3.15 mm sheet lead are fixe to the sheet lead by plumbers solder or leadburning.
(b) The face end of the tack is then passed through a prepared opening in the timber boarding.
(c) Finally, the free end of the tack is turned down on the inside and secured by a brass or copper plate and two brass screws.

Note. On account of the greater provision for expansion and contraction of the sheet lead, the secret tack is superior to the solder dot.

Continuous Tack, Fig. 4 An excellent method of fixing the edges of sheet lead timber, allowing expansion and contraction and preventing lifting in a strong wind.

(a) The tack is copper nailed along the boarding edge as shown.
(b) A welt is formed on the edge of the sheet lead covering the edge of the ta tack.
(c) The sheet lead is turned down over the vertical boarding.

Bale Tack, Fig. 5 Used to fix the free edge of cover or stepped flashing. The tacks made from 2.50-3.15 mm sheet lead 38 mm wide are fitted over the upstand prior to fixing the flashing.

Lead Dot, Fig. 6 Used to fix sheet lead to concrete or stone cornices, copings etc.

(a) The mason cuts a dovetail hole in the stone or concrete.
(b) The plumber then lays the sheet lead, having noted the positions of the holes.
(c) A hole is made in the sheet lead and the lead worked up 9.520 mm high with the bent bolt and hammer.
(d) A special cast iron mould is placed over the hole and lead which is just molten poured into the top of the mould.
(e) The mould is removed and after the lead has cooled the dot is caulked with a mallet.

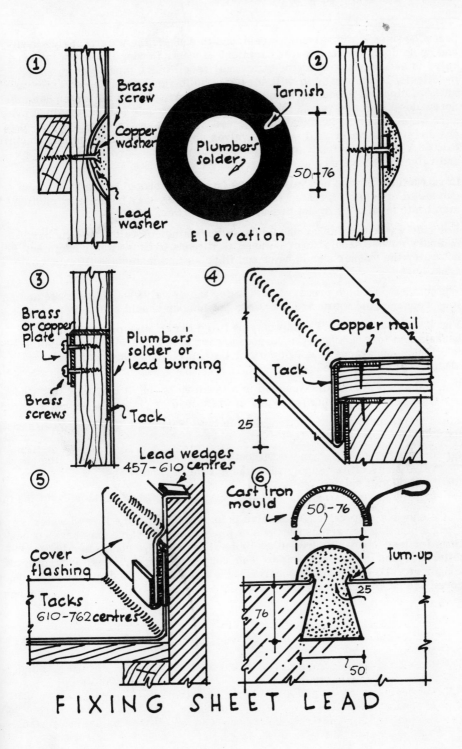

① Brass screw
Copper washer
Lead washer

Tarnish
Plumber's solder
50-76
Elevation

②
50-76

③ Brass or copper plate
Plumber's solder or lead burning
Brass screws
Tack

④ Copper nail
Tack
25

⑤ Lead wedges 457-610 centres
Cover flashing
Tacks 610-762 centres

⑥ Cast iron mould
50-76
Turn-up
25
76
50

FIXING SHEET LEAD

Screw Down Taps and Valves

Screw down taps and valves are designed to shut off the water supply slowly and by so doing prevent 'water hammer'. If water flowing through a tap or valve is suddenly arrested, the water will recoil in the pipe. Water, being practically incompressible, will act like a solid ram, setting up stresses inside the pipe and producing a noise like hammering known as 'water hammer'. Screw down taps and valves tend to prevent this trouble but on very high pressure water supply it is sometimes necessary to fix an air vessel to provide a cushion for the water. All taps and valves should be tested by the manufacturer to 2068 kPa but as an extra precaution some water authorities require taps and valves to be tested and stamped at their own works.

Constructions of taps and valves Taps and valves should be made of brass, gun metal or other corrosion resisting alloy. They may be made by casting metal into moulds or by hot pressing metal between dies.

For cold water the washer should be either leather or vulcanised rubber; ordinary rubber should never be used as it tends to cause water hammer. For hot water the washer should be of red fibre as this material will withstand great heat.

The jumper on a high pressure cold water tap or valve should be loose and on low pressure cold water and hot water the jumper should be fixed.

Fig. 1 shows a bib tap. The tap may be fitted over a sink or used for filling buckets and for washing down purposes, when it is fitted with a hose union outlet. When appearance is not important, the tap is plain brass and the easy-clean cover is dispensed with.

Fig. 2 shows a pillar tap connected to a lavatory basin. It may also be fitted to a sink or bath. The tap is bedded in white lead or plaster of paris.

Fig. 3 shows an exploded section of a bib type 'Supertap'. The tap possesses the following features:

(a) the washer can be changed without turning off the water supply (the check valve shuts off the supply when the nozzle is removed);
(b) built-in anti splash;
(c) finger light operation.

Fig. 4 shows a stop valve. This valve is used to control the flow of water along a pipeline or various sections of pipework. The valve may have connections for lead, copper or iron pipes or be fitted to allow connection between different types of pipe, e.g. lead to lead, copper to copper, iron to iron, iron to copper etc. To give a good appearance the tap may be fitted with an easy clean cover and be chromium plated.

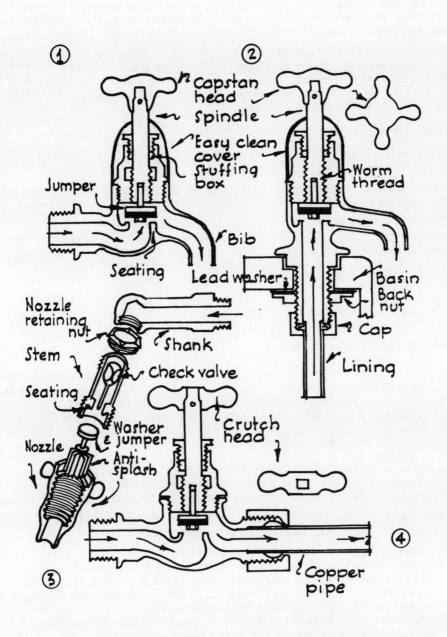

① Capstan head
Spindle
Easy clean cover
Stuffing box
Jumper
Seating
Bib

② Worm thread
Lead washer
Basin Back nut
Cap
Lining

③ Nozzle retaining nut
Stem
Shank
Check valve
Seating
Nozzle
Washer & jumper
Anti-splash
Crutch head

④ Copper pipe

SCREW-DOWN TAPS & VALVES

Ball Valves

The purpose of a ball valve is to regulate automatically the supply of water to a cistern. The valve shuts off the supply of water when the water reaches the required level.

The valve works on the principle of a lever, Fig. 1. When the float is in the lower position, the valve is fully open and water enters the cistern. As the cistern fills the ball becomes buoyant and exerts an upward thrust which is transmitted via the lever to the plunger; this gradually closes against the seating and shuts off the supply of water.

TYPES OF VALVES

There are four types, namely: (a) Portsmouth, (b) Croydon, (c) B.R.S., i.e. Building Research Station, (d) Equilibrium.

Portsmouth and Croydon types The piston or plunger in the Portsmouth type, Fig. 2, moves horizontally, whereas in the Croydon type the plunger moves vertically Fig. 3.

The diameter of the orifice is a very important factor and governs the type of valve, i.e. whether high medium or low pressure. The high pressure ball valve orifice is about 3.2 mm dia, the medium pressure about 6.4 mm dia and the low pressure is fullway, i.e. 13 mm or 19 mm dia.

The Model Bylaws Series X.X.1. (which deal with the prevention of waste, undue consumption, misuse or contamination of water) contain, in clause 25, the following matter relative to ball valves.

(a) Portsmouth type ball valves not exceeding 51 mm diameter to comply with B.S. 1212: 1953. Fig. 2 shows the B.S. 1212: 1953 valve.

(b) Valves not of the Portsmouth type to be sound, suitable, and comply with the following regulations:

(i) High pressure valve to close against a test pressure 1378.96 kPa medium pressure valve against 689.48 kPa low pressure valve against 275.79 kPa. These valves should have the letters H.P., M.P. or L.P. cast or stamped on the body of the valve. Every valve shall be capable of resisting a pressure of 2068.44 kPa.

(ii) Washer to be of vulcanised rubber or other suitable material.

(iii) Body and piston to be of a corrosion resisting alloy.

(iv) Valve exceeding 51 mm dia, a flange on its inlet, to be provided.

B.R.S. Valve The Building Research Station have designed a valve with excellent features, Fig. 4. The advantages of the valve are:

(a) Larger lever ratio and therefore greater efficiency.

(b) More silence in action as there is no splashing in the cistern.
It is claimed to make a quarter the noise of the B.S. 1212: 1953 valve.

(c) Less trouble with sticking; the pistons in the Portsmouth and Croydon types often corrode and stick to the body of the valve.

(d) The water level is adjusted without bending the lever. The adjustment is by means of a thumbscrew and tools are not required.

Equilibrium Valve, Fig. 5 The principle of the valve is to transmit equal water pressures to both ends of the piston thus reducing considerably the force required by the lever. The valve is most suitable for very high pressure supplies where there is a possibility of water hammer.

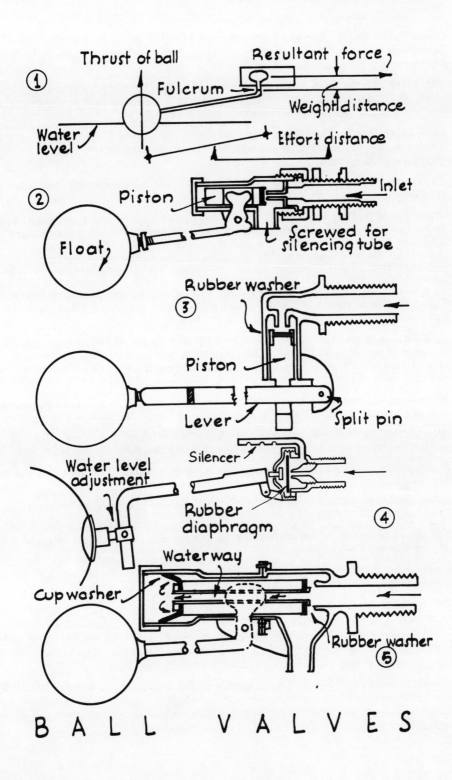

① Thrust of ball — Resultant force — Fulcrum — Weight distance — Water level — Effort distance

② Piston — Inlet — Screwed for silencing tube — Float

③ Rubber washer — Piston — Lever — Split pin

④ Silencer — Water level adjustment — Rubber diaphragm — Cup washer

⑤ Waterway — Rubber washer

BALL VALVES

Valves and Cocks

Globe Valve, Fig. 1 Are similar in construction to the ordinary stop valve described in pages 51 and 52, they are however more robust and may be used for very high pressure steam or water.

The valve may be used for insertion in a pipe line to control various sections of piping or used as a radiator valve, in which case there is a metal to metal seating and the valve may be either straight or angular.

Gate Valve, Fig. 2 The Globe Valve may produce a poor flow of water on low pressure, due to the friction set up when the water passes through the seating and changes direction.

To reduce this loss of flow on pressure pipe lines a full-way gate valve should be used.

Operation of Valve The valve is operated by the raising and lowering of the gate. The gate is made from either one or two wedge shaped metal discs which lift clear of the opening when the valve is fully opened. When the valve is fully closed the discs make a metal to metal contact with the valve seating and prevents the flow of water, steam etc.

Plug Cock, Fig. 3 Is used to control the flow of gas or low pressure water. The cock should never be used for controlling high pressure water, or water hammer will be produced by the quick closing of the cock.

Operation of cock The cock is operated by turning the tapering plug through an angle of 45° (quarter turn). The plug has a hole cast or drilled through the middle, and when the cock is turned to the 'on' position this hole is brought into line with the flow.

When the cock is turned to the 'off' position, the hole moves across the direction of flow and the solid portion of the plug prevents the flow of gas or water.

It is always advisable to take out the plug of a new cock and smear the contacting surfaces with tallow. This will lubricate the cock and prevent leakage.

Fig. 4 shows a draining plug cock with a hose end outlet. The cock is used for draining boilers, cylinders, sections of pipework etc.

Safety valve, Fig. 5 and 6 Is used to relieve excess pressure on boilers, cylinders etc.

There are a variety of valves but the most common used in plumbing are the spring and deadweight types.

Spring loaded valves are normally used for small domestic boilers and deadweight valves for large heating boilers.

The loadings on the valves should be adjusted to 10 per cent greater than the pressure of water produced by the static head above the valve. In the case of a deadweight valve this is easily calculated, but with the spring valve the valve is adjusted by the manufacturers.

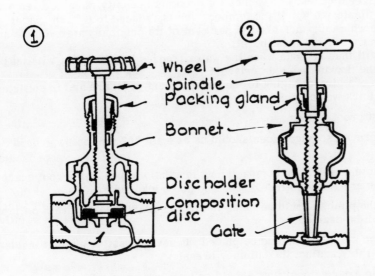

1.
Wheel
Spindle
Packing gland
Bonnet
Disc holder
Composition disc

2.
Gate

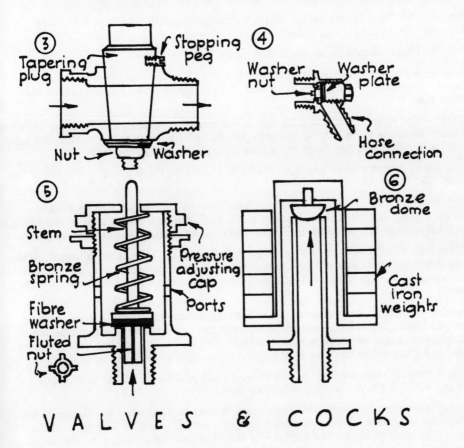

3.
Tapering plug
Stopping peg
Nut
Washer

4.
Washer nut
Washer plate
Hose connection

5.
Stem
Bronze spring
Fibre washer
Fluted nut
Pressure adjusting cap
Ports

6.
Bronze dome
Cast iron weights

VALVES & COCKS

Protection from Frost and Loss of Heat

Mechanics of freezing Water reaches its maximum density when at a temperature of approximately 4 °C. If the temperature is reduced to 0 °C the water changes to ice which expands about 9 per cent of its original water volume and this expansion causes the frost burst.

The damage will thus be done when the water freezes but the burst will not be noticed until the thawing period arrives.

The expansion of water changing to ice causes great pressure and is sufficient to burst even thick walled pipes and vessels.

Design of frost proof system

Fig. 1—Underground service pipes should be at least 762 mm below ground level.

Fig. 2—The system should be compact; long lengths of pipes in the roof space or under floors are liable to freeze, and should be avoided

The whole of the piping should be made to fall to suitably placed drain off taps so that they can be drained.

Pipes, tanks and cylinders should be placed whenever possible against inside walls, or preferably against the chimney breast.

Fig. 3—Pipes in exposed positions should be well lagged.

Fig. 4—The lagging should be carried through the wall and kept dry. Wet lagging has no insulation value.

Fig. 5—Pipes should be at least 2 m away from the eaves.

Fig. 6—A copper draught flap should be fixed to bath overflows, the overflow from cold water storage cisterns and W.C. cisterns should be dipped at the inlet end.

Fig. 7—The hole where the bath waste and overflow pipes pass through the wall should be made good before the bath panels are fixed. In many cases this has been neglected and has been the cause of many frost bursts.

The hot and cold supply pipes to the bath should be fixed along the front of the bath.

Fig. 8—Cold water storage cisterns fixed in roof spaces should be well insulated and placed above the airing cupboard. A small hole made in the ceiling will allow heat from the airing cupboard to pass through to the cistern.

Pipes etc. should be fixed clear of air bricks and cold draughts avoided. With regard to soil and waste pipes, internal stacks will not freeze unless exposed to draughts and for this reason alone, internal stacks are preferable to external ones.

Insulation against loss of heat Good insulation prevents heat losses, saves fuel and soon repays its cost. Hot water tanks and cylinders should be insulated by a jacket or other suitable means, Fig. 9. Ideally all hot water pipes should be insulated but this is not always possible because it is unsightly.

Pipes may be insulated by means of sectional plastic or mineral-wool, or by wrapping with fibre glass or mineral-wool.

Large pipes and hot water storage vessels may be insulated by magnesia or plastic compounds. Water is added to these until a paste is formed and the material applied whilst the surface of the pipe or tank is hot, wire netting being inserted for reinforcement, Fig. 10.

57

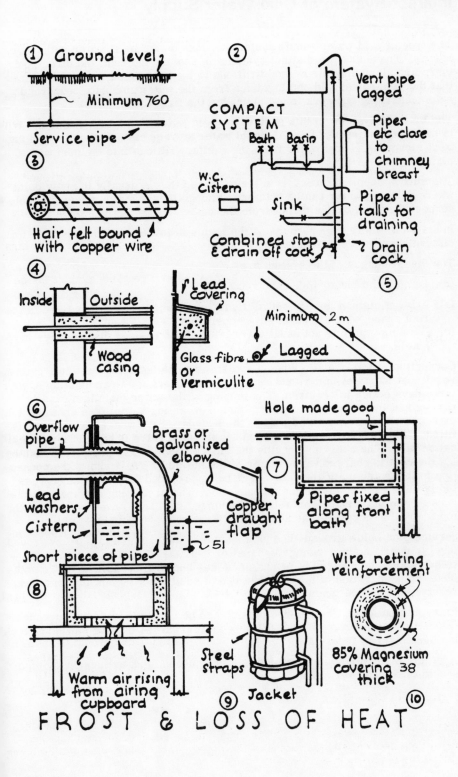

① Ground level

Minimum 760

Service pipe

② COMPACT SYSTEM

Vent pipe lagged

Bath Basin

Pipes etc close to chimney breast

W.C. Cistern

Sink

Pipes to falls for draining

Combined stop & drain off cock

Drain cock

③ Hair felt bound with copper wire

④ Inside Outside

Wood casing

Lead covering

Glass fibre or vermiculite

⑤ Minimum 2 m

Lagged

⑥ Overflow pipe

Brass or galvanised elbow

Lead washers

Cistern

Short piece of pipe

Copper draught flap

51

Hole made good

⑦ Pipes fixed along front bath

⑧ Warm air rising from airing cupboard

⑨ Steel straps

Jacket

Wire netting reinforcement

⑩ 85% Magnesium covering 38 thick

FROST & LOSS OF HEAT

Indirect System of Cold Water Supply

The type of cold water supply system depends on the local water authorities bylaws. There are two distinct systems in use, i.e. indirect, and direct, but there are also some slight modifications to these systems, and it is essentia that the plumber should obtain advice from the water authority concerned before carrying out work in a district for the first time.

The Indirect System In this system the cold water to the bath, basin and W.C is supplied 'indirectly' from the cold water storage cistern, thus preventing back siphonage of foul water from the sanitary fittings into the company's main.

The sink is supplied direct from the main and this is usually the only point where drinking water can be obtained although it is sometimes permissable t connect the wash basins direct from the main.

In districts where the pressure on the mains is low or intermittent the stora cistern ensures a constant supply of water.

The disadvantages of the system are:

(a) Larger and longer pipes are required.

(b) A large cistern is required, difficult to accommodate unless fixed in the roof space, which is generally undesirable.

(c) Drinking water is not usually available at the basin, a disadvantage in hotels.

Connection to water main When a system is to be installed the water compar require at least seven days notice, and for an alteration to an existing systerr three days notice is required. The tapping of the water main is normally carried out by the water company, who screw a plug tap into the crown of the main and run the service pipe up to the boundary wall where a stop valve is fitted. This pipe from the water main to the stop valve is called the communi cation pipe. The company provide the pipe, stop valve and protecting chambe but the cost is charged to the owner of the building. Fig. 1 shows the connec-tion to the water main, the goose neck being provided to relieve any stress likely to be exerted on the main connection. The protecting chamber may be constructed of brick or concrete, and a hinged cast iron cover is fitted at the top to provide access to the stop valve.

Service pipe below ground The pipe should be at least 762 mm below ground level to guard against damage by frost or heavy traffic. The bottom of the trench should be cleared of bricks or stones and well consolidated. To com-plete the preparation of the trench, a bed of sand about 50 mm thick is laid to receive the service pipe.

Entry into building The service pipe should be carried inside the building so that the rising main is at least 610 mm away from the outside wall, thus avoi ing the danger of freezing.

A 76 mm diameter stoneware pipe is laid to accommodate the service pipe should this need ever arise.

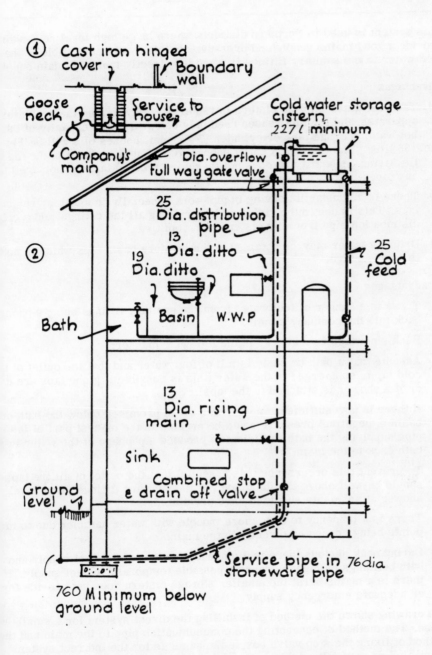

① Cast iron hinged cover
Boundary wall
Goose neck
Service to house
Company's main

Cold water storage cistern
227ℓ minimum

Dia.overflow
Full way gate valve

②
25 Dia. distribution pipe
13 Dia. ditto
19 Dia. ditto

Basin
W.W.P

25 Cold feed

Bath

13 Dia. rising main

Sink
Combined stop e drain off valve

Ground level

Service pipe in 76dia stoneware pipe

760 Minimum below ground level

INDIRECT SYSTEM OF COLD WATER SUPPLY

Direct System of Cold Water Supply

This system is used in Northern districts where large high level reservoir provide a good mains supply and pressure. In this system the whole of the cold water to the sanitary fittings is provided directly from the main suppl

Advantages

(a) The cold water storage cistern is required solely to feed the hot water apparatus, and for this reason need only be equal to the capacity of the hot water storage tank or cylinder. For small houses this will be 114 136 litre. The cistern is small enough to be accommodated in the top the airing cupboard, and does not therefore require lagging, nor are th any pipes in the roof space.

(b) There is a substantial saving in pipework especially in multi-storey bu ings. This is due to the rising main supplying all the fittings, and a col distribution pipe from the cistern being omitted.

(c) Drinking water may be obtained at the lavatory basin taps which in hot is an advantage.

Disadvantages

(a) There is a danger of foul water from the sanitary fittings being siphone back into the company's main.

Back siphonage could occur in the following manner:

Assume that a bath or basin is full of foul water and that the outlet of t cold tap is submerged in the water (this is possible if globe taps are us or if a shower is attached to the taps).

If there is now sufficient water drawn off in premises below the bath o basin a 'negative' pressure could be created in the highest part of the pipe supplying the bath, sufficient to produce siphonage of the water in bath back to the main.

To prevent this occurrence it is essential that the outlet of all the taps should be well above the flood level of the sanitary fittings. **Low level** shower attachments should also be prohibited.

(b) There is a tendency to have more trouble with water hammer due to me points being connected directly to the main.

(c) During peak periods there is a tendency for the lowering of supply and with buildings on higher ground a possible temporary loss of supply. If there is a mains burst the smaller storage cistern does not provide for an adequate emergency supply.

The drawing shows the method of installing the direct system for a small house. The method of connecting the communication pipe to the main and the method of fixing the stop valve box, is the same as for the indirect system illustrated on page 59 and 60.

The best system of cold water supply is a modified indirect.

In this system the lavatory basins and the sinks are supplied directly from main, but all other sanitary fittings are supplied from a cold water storage cistern. This method provides drinking water at the basins, which is desirab for all types of buildings.

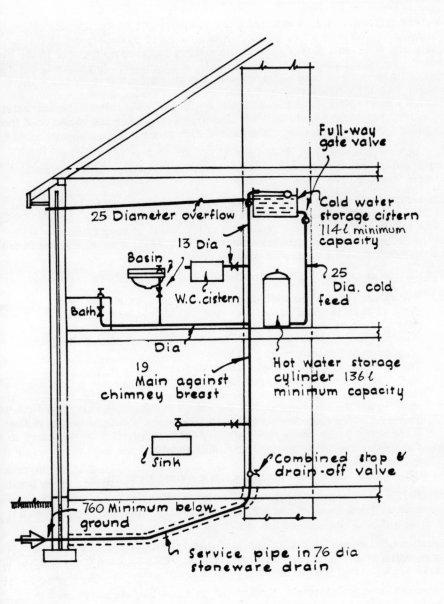

Full-way
gate valve

25 Diameter overflow

Cold water
storage cistern
114ℓ minimum
capacity

13 Dia

Basin

W.C. cistern

25
Dia. cold
feed

Bath

Dia

19
Main against
chimney breast

Hot water storage
cylinder 136ℓ
minimum capacity

Sink

Combined stop &
drain-off valve

760 Minimum below
ground

Service pipe in 76 dia
stoneware drain

DIRECT SYSTEM
OF COLD WATER
SUPPLY

Cold Water Storage and Expansion Cisterns

Storage cistern, Fig. 1 A storage cistern, in an indirect system of cold wat supply, supplies cold water to the hot water tank or cylinder, and to the bat basin and W.C. In a direct system the cistern supplies cold water to the ho water tank or cylinder only. The capacity of the cistern therefore is deter- mined by the type of cold water system; for an indirect system a minimum capacity of 227 litre is required, whilst a direct system needs a minimum capacity of 114 litre, i.e. at least equal to the capacity of the hot water tank cylinder. For larger buildings the capacity of the cistern is based upon the number and type of sanitary fittings, and the probable demand on them.

For large cisterns, above 4546 litre, it is advisable to install two cisterns i duplicate so that if one cistern has to be cleaned out or repaired the other cistern can keep the system in use.

Expansion cistern, Fig. 2 For a small heating system in a house the capacit of the cistern is usually 45 litre. For larger heating systems the capacity should be based on the total expansion of the water in the system i.e. the wa in the boiler, pipes and radiators, plus $33\frac{1}{3}$ per cent. This expansion shoul take place within the expansion space.

Installation of cistern. The following are the main points to remember:

(a) The cistern should be well supported; 227 litre weighs 227 kg.
(b) If the cistern is fixed in the roof space, it should be kept away from the eaves, adjacent to the chimney breast and well insulated.
(c) The inlet and outlet connections should be at opposite ends to prevent stagnation of the water.
(d) The ball-tap should be fixed as high as possible.
(e) The centre line of the overflow should be at least 40 mm below the cent line of the ball-tap. This is a precaution against back siphonage of the water from the cistern into the mains.
(f) The cold water distribution and cold feed pipes should be connected not more than 50 mm above the bottom of the cistern.
(g) The water line when the cistern is full should be not less than 25 mm b the invert of the overflow pipe.
(h) Cisterns should have a dust proof, but not air tight, cover.

Installation of an expansion cistern The connections to the cistern are exac the same as for a storage cistern. The water line however, when the water i cold, should be 50 mm above the feed pipe connection.

Location of cisterns In high class work cisterns are fixed in a special ciste room which is easily accessible, well lighted, ventilated and heated. In ordi house work the cistern is fixed in the roof space or at ceiling level.

Materials used for cisterns Galvanised mild steel is normally used but car is needed with copper pipes or electrolytic corrosion will occur. After fixir filings etc. should be removed and the inside given 2 coats of bituminous pai Plastic and asbestos cement cisterns are also used.

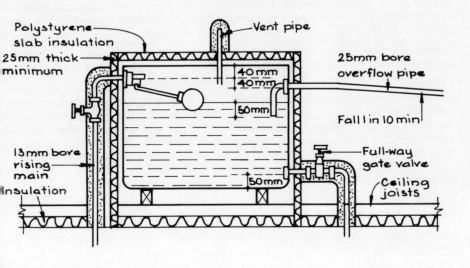

①

Polystyrene slab insulation 25mm thick minimum

Vent pipe

25mm bore overflow pipe

40 mm
40 mm
50 mm

Fall 1 in 10 min

Full-way gate valve

13mm bore rising main

Insulation

50mm

Ceiling joists

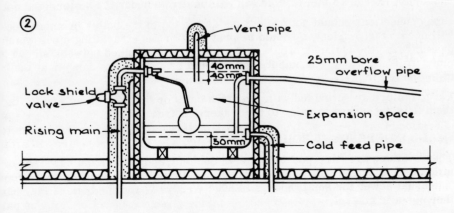

②

Vent pipe

25mm bore overflow pipe

40 mm
40 mm

Expansion space

Lock shield valve

Rising main

50mm

Cold feed pipe

COLD WATER STORAGE AND
EXPANSION & FEED CISTERNS

Back and Small Independent Boilers

BACK BOILERS

A back or range boiler is fitted behind the fireplace and is used to provide h water for a small house.

The metal used for the boiler depends upon the type of water, and is governe by the local water authorities bylaws. Copper or stainless steel is used in soft water districts as no discolouration of the water occurs. Wrought iron, cast iron, or mild steel boilers are used in hard water districts and may be rust proofed by Bower Barffing. They are provided with a handhole to allow periodical cleaning.

Types The small type back boiler is either a plain rectangular type Fig. 1 o an arched flue type, Fig. 2. Large back boilers vary greatly in design; some have built in flue ways, Fig. 3, others fins or tubes.

The object in designing a back, or any, type of boiler, is to expose as much a possible of the boiler plate to the fire or flue gases. The boiler plate expose direct to the fire is known as 'direct heating surface' and the boiler plate ex posed to the hot flue gases as 'indirect heating surface'. In designing the in direct heating surface it is important to provide a comparatively narrow space so that the flue gases come into close contact with the boiler plate and a 'scrubbing' action occurs between the plate and the flue gases.

Rating An accurate power rating for a back boiler is not always given becau of varying types of fuel, amount of draught and sizes of fire.

Small boilers have a maximum power of 2 700 W-3 300 W and an average pow of 1 500-1 800 W.

Large boilers can usually heat 136 litre of water plus one or two radiators.

Fixing Fig. 6 shows how to fix the boiler; the flue height under the boiler should not exceed 76 mm or cold air will be drawn under the boiler.

Pipe connections should not project inside the top of the boiler or an air lock will occur, Fig. 5. Sleeves should be provided for the circulating pipes which pass through the chimney breast, and mineral-wool caulked between sleeve a pipe. To control the heat output, there should be an efficient damper at the tc of the boiler flue.

Large boilers are provided with firebrick units or 'built in' flues, and to fix them it is necessary to refer to the makers instructions.

SMALL INDEPENDENT BOILERS

These boilers are 'fire-pot' type, i.e. in one unit, and made from cast iron or mild steel, which, in soft water districts, should be Bower Barffing rust proof The usual power for small houses is 6000 W-9000 W and the boilers may hav thermostatic control.

Fixing, Fig. 8 A suitable hearth should be provided, preferably of tiles on cor crete 152 mm thick. The concrete should project 305 mm in front and 229 m on either side of the boiler. The wall at the back should be of non-combustib material and extend 914 mm above the top and 305 mm on either side of the boiler. Combustible material must be more than 229 mm from flue pipe. Fig 7 shows how to connect the flue pipe to a brick chimney.

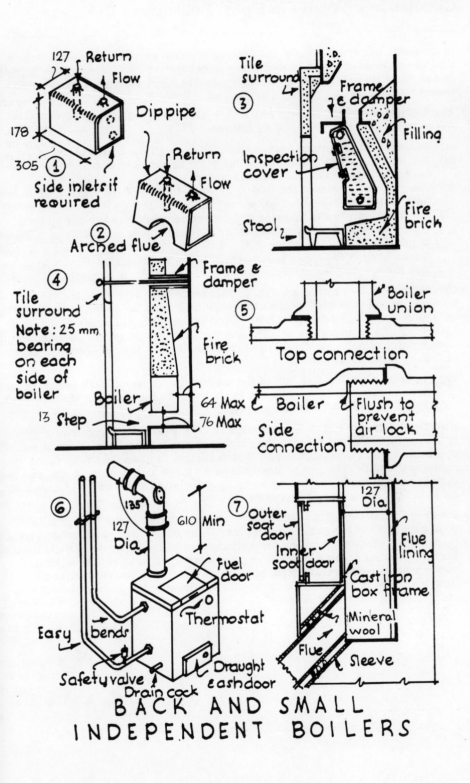

127 Return
Flow

Dip pipe

178

305 ①

Side inlets if
required

② Arched flue

Return
Flow

③ Tile surround
Frame & damper
Filling
Inspection cover
Stool₂
Fire brick

④ Tile surround
Note: 25 mm bearing on each side of boiler
Frame & damper
Fire brick
Boiler
13 Step
64 Max
76 Max

⑤ Boiler union
Top connection

Boiler
Flush to prevent air lock
Side connection

⑥ 135
127 Dia
610 Min
Fuel door
Thermostat
Easy bends
Safety valve
Drain cock
Draught & ashdoor

⑦ Outer soot door
Inner soot door
127 Dia
Flue lining
Cast iron box frame
Mineral wool
Flue
Sleeve

BACK AND SMALL
INDEPENDENT BOILERS

Circulation of Water in Pipes, Boilers and Cylinders

In domestic hot water supply and heating systems relying on gravity circula-tion, the movement of the heated water is brought about by convection current These currents are set up by the difference in density between water at dif-ferent temperatures.

Fig. 1 shows a simple system with boiler, circulating pipes and cylinder. The water in the cylinder is heated as follows:

(a) radiant heat from the fire is conducted through the boiler plate.
(b) the water in contact with the boiler plate becomes heated and therefore becomes less dense than the cold water.
(c) the cold water pushes the heated water to the top of the boiler and as mo heat is applied, the water passes up the flow pipe.
(d) hot water enters the cylinder and convection currents are set up until warm water eventually passes down the return pipe, and being at a lower temperature than the water in the flow pipe, and therefore heavier, it con tinues to push the water being heated in the boiler up the flow pipe and into the cylinder until all the water in the cylinder is heated.

Circulating pressure or head, Fig. 2 This is the pressure of water creating circulation and is caused by the difference in density between the vertical flo column and vertical return column. If we assume that the water in the flow column is at a temperature of 71°C and the water in the return column is at a temperature of 49°C, the circulating pressure will be the difference in density of these two water columns.

Dip in return pipe, Fig 3 A dip in the return pipe causes a back pressure and should be avoided. If however a dip is unavoidable the extent of the dip shoul not exceed ⅙th of the circulating height.

High level returns, Fig. 4 This system is very useful for bungalows where it is impossible to avoid running the return pipe under the floor. The circulatin pressure set up in columns A and B is sufficient to overcome resistance in columns C and D. The height H should be as large as possible. A direct cylinder would cause trouble by stopping circulation when water is drawn off. An indirect cylinder must therefore be used.

Reverse Circulation This takes place when the water in the flow pipe is cooler than the water in the return pipe. If the boiler fire is allowed to go out circulation between the boiler and cylinder gradually slows down until it stops There is now cold water in the flow pipe, when the fire is relighted, heated water passes up the return pipe, because of the colder, heavier water in the flow pipe. The trouble can be corrected by allowing the system to cool down and relighting the boiler fire.

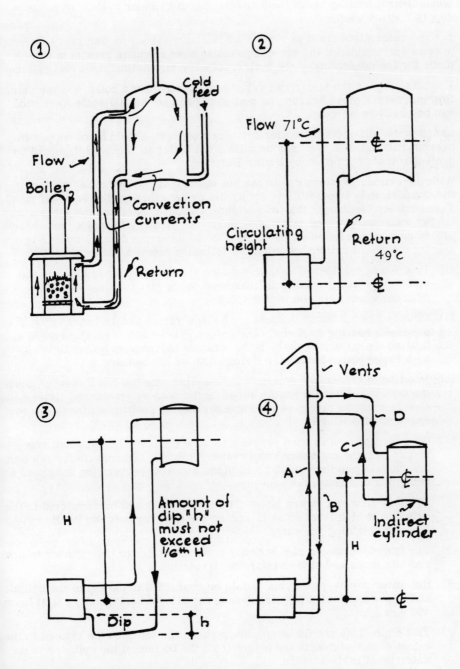

① Cold feed

Flow

Boiler

Convection currents

Return

② Flow 71°C

Circulating height

Return 49°C

③ Amount of dip "h" must not exceed 1/6th H

H

Dip

h

④ Vents

A

B

C

D

H

Indirect cylinder

CIRCULATION OF WATER

Direct Cylinder System of Hot Water Supply

When central heating is not installed the direct cylinder system of hot water supply may be used.

In hard water districts it is always advisable to install the indirect system to prevent furring, and if the direct system is used adequate provision must be made for the de-scaling of the boiler, primary circulating pipes and cylinder

For this purpose the boiler and cylinder must have hand holes, and the prima flow and return pipes access plugs at each bend so that all scale formation can be easily removed.

In soft water districts the boiler cylinder and pipes should be of copper to prevent rusting. If a cast iron or mild steel boiler is required it should be protected from corrosion by Bower Barffing.

With the cylinder system, due to the hot water being drawn off at the top of the cylinder, it is impossible to empty the system through the draw off taps. This obviates the danger that was attendant with the earlier tank system when the hot water supply pipe was connected to the primary flow pipe, and thereby providing a means by which the system could be emptied accidentally. In designing the direct cylinder system the following points must be observed.

(a) Position of cylinder—The best position for the cylinder is close to the boiler, this will prevent heat losses from the circulation pipes. The cylinder should also be well insulated.

(b) Boiler—The hot water demand for houses varies widely, but it is usual to assume a heating up period of $1\frac{1}{2}$-2 hr. There are several methods of heating the water, the most usual being an independent boiler in the kitch or a range boiler behind the living room or kitchen fire.

(c) Position of cold water storage cistern—Since the head of the water above the taps is obtained from the height of the cold water storage cistern, the cistern must be placed in the highest possible position either in the roof space or at ceiling level.

(d) Cold feed pipe—It is good practice to have the cold feed pipe one size larger than the hot water supply pipe. This will compensate for friction losses set up in the cylinder and pipes, and also prevent the danger of air being drawn through the vent pipe.

(e) Primary flow and return pipes—The flow pipe should be connected to the cylinder at high level so as to reduce the time lag between lighting the fire and obtaining hot water.

The two pipes should rise steadily from the boiler to the cylinder to prevent air locks and also to improve circulation.

(f) Hot water supply pipe—This should be connected to the top of the cylinder and to prevent 'one pipe' circulation, run almost horizontally for at least 450 mm.

(g) Vent Pipe—This should be continued above the water in the cistern to the extent of one-sixteenth the height from the bottom of the cylinder to the water level in the cistern.

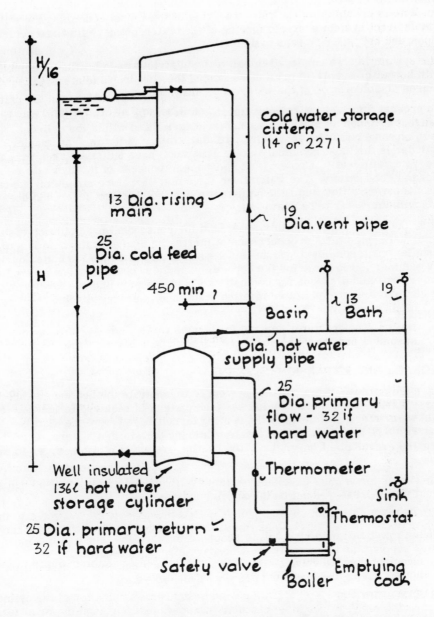

H/16

Cold water storage
cistern -
114 or 227 l

13 Dia. rising
main

19
Dia. vent pipe

25
Dia. cold feed
pipe

H

450 min

Basin

13
Bath

19

Dia. hot water
supply pipe

25
Dia. primary
flow - 32 if
hard water

Well insulated
136l hot water
storage cylinder

Thermometer

Sink

25 Dia. primary return -
32 if hard water

Thermostat

Safety valve

Boiler

Emptying
cock

DIRECT CYLINDER
SYSTEM OF H.W. SUPPLY

Indirect System of Hot Water Supply

When water of a temporary hard nature is heated to between 49°C and 71°C, the lime is precipitated and causes furring of the vessel containing the water The indirect system prevents furring of the boiler, primary flow and return pipes, and hot water storage cylinder.

The system is also employed in soft water districts when heating is combined with hot water supply, to prevent rusting of the cast iron radiators, which causes discolouration of the water to be drawn off.

To prevent furring or discolouration, the water to be drawn off is heated in the indirect cylinder by means of a heat exchanger fitted within the cylinder. The heat exchanger may be an annular cylinder, coil or radiator. The annular cylinder is the most commonly used. This must have sufficient area to heat the water efficiently. Copper is the best metal because of its high rate of thermal conductivity. The water from the boiler therefore simply circulates via the primary flow and return pipes through the heat exchanger, and does no mix with the water to be drawn off.

After the initial heating of this water, and the consequent precipitation of the lime, there is no further occurrence of furring or discolouration. In large installations a combined system is not satisfactory because the boiler during the summer is too large for the hot water supply. For this reason either two boilers are installed, one for domestic hot water supply and one for heating, o an electric immersion heater is fitted inside the indirect cylinder.

BOILER

In a combined system this is usually an independent type although in a small system a large range boiler may be used.

STORAGE AND EXPANSION CISTERNS

Since the purpose of the indirect system is to separate the heating and hot water supply water, an expansion and feed cistern is required in addition to a cold water storage cistern. If the heating circuit is fed from the storage cistern there is danger of rusty water entering the storage cistern. In addition, the expansion of the water in the heating system may cause water to over flow.

The two cisterns must have their water levels approximately equal so that equal water pressures act on the annular cylinder.

SECONDARY CIRCUIT

When a towel rail or airing coil is required, or when the length of the hot water supply pipe is excessive, a secondary circuit is required.
A convenient throttle valve on the secondary return enables the circulation to be shut off during the night, and prevents heat losses.

HEATING CIRCUIT

This may be either single or two pipe for a gravity circuit; with some modifications the Small-Bore forced system may be used.
A valve should be fitted on the return so that the circulation through the heating system may be shut off during the summer when the boiler and indirect cylinder only are in operation.
Fig. 1 shows a typical indirect system combined with a heating circuit. It will be noticed that the primary circuit on the right hand side is entirely separate from the hot water supply, and secondary circuit, on the left hand side.

71

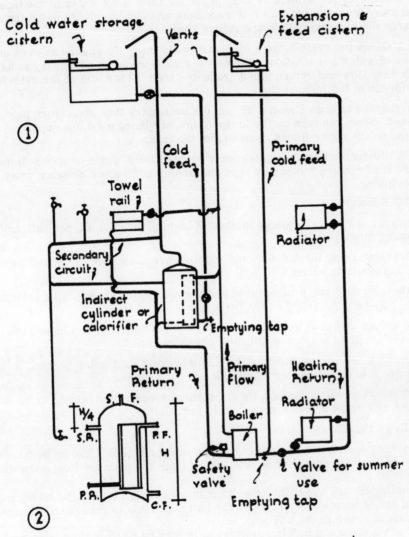

Cold water storage cistern

Vents

Expansion & feed cistern

①

Cold feed

Primary cold feed

Towel rail

Radiator

Secondary circuit

Indirect cylinder or calorifier

Emptying tap

Primary Return

Primary Flow

Heating Return

Radiator

②

S. F.

W/4

S. R.

P. F.

H

Boiler

Safety valve

Valve for summer use

P. R.

C. F.

Emptying tap

C. F.	Cold feed	P. R.	Primary return
P. F.	Primary flow	S. R.	Secondary return
S. F.	Secondary flow		

INDIRECT
SYSTEM OF HOT WATER SUPPLY

Combined Cylinder and Tank System of Hot Water Suppl

The combined cylinder tank system is used in larger buildings such as hotels flats, schools, factories etc.

The purpose of the system is to improve the flow of hot water at the taps far- thest away from the hot water storage tank or cylinder, and to avoid long runs of large dia secondary flow and return pipes.

Fig. 1 shows the system for a four-storey building. To ensure an even distri- bution of water at each floor without the tank it would be necessary to have the secondary flow and return pipes graduated from 32 mm dia at the cylinder to 19 mm dia at the highest floor.

By fixing the tank as shown a 25 mm dia secondary flow and return pipe may be used. When the taps on the lower floors are being used, the supply of water to taps on the upper floors comes from the tank.

Fig. 2 illustrates how the system may be used for a single-storey building where it is required to supply taps that are situated some distance away from the cylinder.

SHOWER BATHS

This is a much more hygienic method of bathing than the slipper bath and is becoming more popular.

It is essential that the hot and cold supplies are automatically mixed together by a thermostatic valve.

If a thermostatic valve is not used and the cold water supply fails, scalding water may be discharged on the bather.

Some valves will operate under as low a head of water as 1.5 m, and the hot and cold supplies may have different pressures.

The non-return valves fitted on the inlets prevent cold water passing through the valve into the hot water supply pipe or vice-versa.

Fig. 3 shows an elevation of a thermostatically controlled mixing valve for a shower and Fig. 4 shows a shower bath installation.

DRYING COILS

Whenever possible the hot water storage tank or cylinder should be fixed clos to the boiler to prevent undue heat losses from the primary flow and return pipes.

In smaller houses the cylinder or tank is invariably fixed in the airing cup- board either inside or adjacent to the bathroom; this is necessary because of the lack of space in the kitchen.

In larger houses and hotels however, coils may be fixed in the airing cupboard and the cylinder placed next to the boiler in the basement or boiler house.

Fig. 5 shows a system with coils for the airing cupboard. These coils should preferably be connected to the domestic hot water side of the system because their connection to the heating side entails restricted use in summer when the heating is unlikely to be used.

Horizontal cylinders It is often more convenient to fix a cylinder in the hori- zontal rather than in the vertical position, e.g. where there is lack of headroom or floor space.

Fig. 6 shows the connections to an indirect and a direct cylinder.

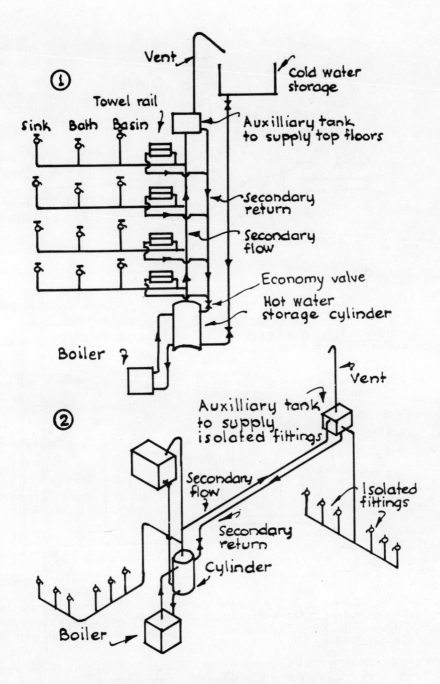

Vent

① Cold water storage

Towel rail

Sink Bath Basin

Auxilliary tank to supply top floors

Secondary return

Secondary flow

Economy valve

Hot water storage cylinder

Boiler ?

② Auxilliary tank to supply isolated fittings

Vent

Secondary flow

Isolated fittings

Secondary return

Cylinder

Boiler →

CYLINDER - TANK SYSTEM

③

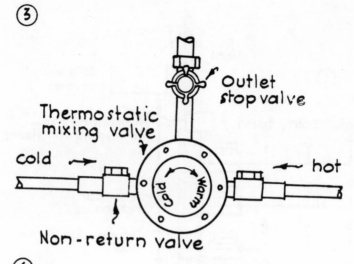

Outlet
stop valve

Thermostatic
mixing valve

cold →

← hot

cold   warm

Non-return valve

④

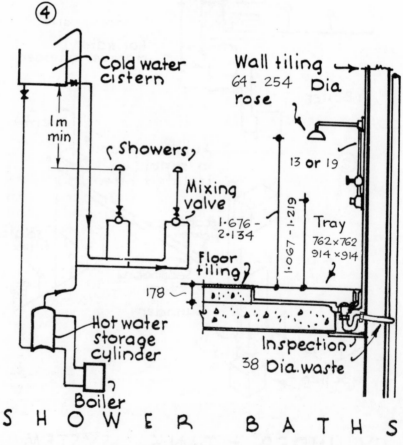

Cold water
cistern

Wall tiling →
64 - 254 Dia
rose

1 m
min

(Showers)

13 or 19

Mixing
valve

1·676 -
2·134

1·067 - 1·219

Tray
762×762
914 ×914

Floor
tiling

178

Hot water
storage
cylinder

Inspection
38 Dia. waste

Boiler

S H O W E R   B A T H S

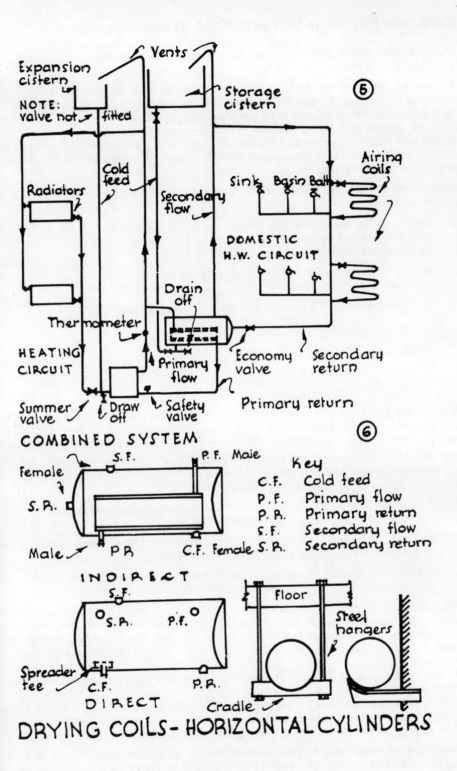

⑤

Vents

Expansion cistern

Storage cistern

NOTE: valve not fitted

Radiators

Cold feed

Secondary flow

Airing coils

Sink Basin Bath

DOMESTIC H.W. CIRCUIT

Thermometer

Drain off

HEATING CIRCUIT

Primary flow

Economy valve

Secondary return

Summer valve   Draw off   Safety valve

Primary return

COMBINED SYSTEM

⑥

S.F.   P.F. Male

Female

Key

C.F. Cold feed
P.F. Primary flow
P.R. Primary return
S.F. Secondary flow
S.R. Secondary return

S.R.

Male   P.R.   C.F. Female S.R.

INDIRECT

S.F.

S.R.   P.F.

Floor

Steel hangers

Spreader tee   C.F.   P.R.

DIRECT

Cradle

DRYING COILS-HORIZONTAL CYLINDERS

Common Faults in Hot and Cold Water Systems

The principal faults are: (a) air locks, (b) insufficient hot water, (c) noises, (d) poor flow of water.

Air Locks, Fig. 1 Water in the system contains suspended air. When the water is heated air is released and rises to the highest point of the system. In a well designed system, where the pipes rise towards the vent pipe at a slc of about 25 mm in 3.000 m the air is released through the vent pipe. Howeve where pipes are dipped or have falls going the wrong way, air is trapped at th highest point preventing the proper flow of water. Fig. 1 shows the most usua positions for air locks.

Insufficient Hot Water This may be due to one, or a combination of the following faults:-

(a) Boiler or hot water storage vessel too small. The power of the boiler may be checked as follows, assuming a 159 litre cylinder, 55 °C temp rise and a 2 hr heat recovery period.

Boiler power in watts $=$ mass flow rate (kg/s)
$\times$ temp rise (°C) $\times$ specific heat capacity of water (J/kg °C).

1 litre of water $=1$ kg mass, therefore mass flow rate (kg/s)
$$=\frac{159}{2 \times 60 \times 60} = 0.022 \text{ kg/s}$$
Boiler power $= 0.022 \times 55 \times 4180$
$$= 5057.8 \text{ J/S or W}$$
$$= 5 \text{ kW approx.}$$

The capacity of the hot water storage vessel may be checked using as a basis the following allowances; bath 68 litre, basin 9 litre, sink 14 litre. If two baths are required in one hour, then $(68 \times 2) + 9 + 14 = 159$ litre cylinder required.

(b) Primary flow and return pipes too long. These should be checked for excessive length, and it might be possible to shorten them by moving the H.W. cylinder or tank nearer to the boiler.

(c) Poor fuel. The use of poor fuel should be discouraged and a suitable fuel to the make of boiler recommended.

(d) Air lock. The fall on the primary flow and return pipes should be checkec by a spirit level, to find if there is an air lock.

(e) Insufficient lagging. Lagging of the hot water storage vessel and the primary flow and return pipes should be recommended.

Noises, Fig. 2 The most serious type is a 'knocking' noise in the primary flow and return pipes or boiler. This is due to imprisoned expanded water caused by freezing, furring or rusting of the pipes. The fire should be withdrawn immediately or an explosion may occur. The pipes should then be descaled or renewed.
A 'knocking' noise in a cold water pipe is caused by water hammer resulting from a faulty valve.
If the ball valve is at fault a larger ball float usually remedies the trouble. In screw down valves, a rubber washer is usually the cause of 'knocking' and this can be corrected by fitting a hard composition washer.

Poor flow of water, Fig. 3 This may be due to (a) an air lock, (b) lack of head, (c) air drawn in through the vent. Fig. 3 shows the latter fault which can be remedied by either using a larger cold feed pipe or raising the storage cister

77

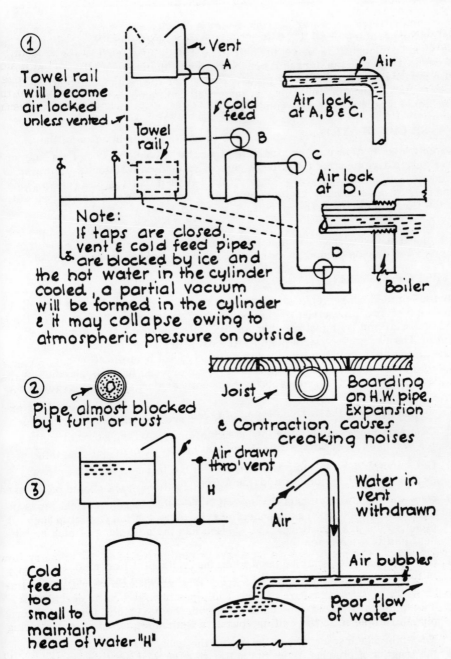

①

Towel rail will become air locked unless vented ➚

Towel rail ➘

Vent
A

Cold feed

Air

Air lock at A, B & C,

B

C

Air lock at D,

Note:
If taps are closed, vent & cold feed pipes are blocked by ice and the hot water in the cylinder cooled, a partial vacuum will be formed in the cylinder & it may collapse owing to atmospheric pressure on outside

D

Boiler

②

Pipe almost blocked by "furr" or rust

Joist ➚

Boarding on H.W. pipe. Expansion & Contraction causes creaking noises

③

Air drawn thro' vent

H

Air

Water in vent withdrawn

Air bubbles

Poor flow of water

Cold feed too small to maintain head of water "H"

COMMON FAULTS IN HOT &
COLD WATER SYSTEMS

Low Temperature Hot Water Heating Systems

Low temperature hot water heating systems usually operate at a maximum water temperature of 80 °C. Water has a high specific heat capacity of 4.2 kJ kg °C and although it is more difficult to heat than other heat transfer media, more heat can be transferred from the boiler to the various heat emitters with relatively small diameter pipes. The higher the temperature of the water the greater is the amount of heat transferred, but some of this heat is lost by the higher heat losses on the pipework.

WATER CIRCULATION

Water in the system may be circulated by natural convection or by means of an electrically operated centrifugal pump. Natural convection of the water is produced by the difference in temperature between the flow and return pipes. The denser cooler water in the return pipe forces the less dense hotter water in the flow pipe through the circuit.

Pumped circulation has now replaced natural convection circulation for all but the smallest installation. Pumped systems have the advantage of providing a shorter heating-up period and also smaller diameter pipes may be used.

TYPES OF SYSTEMS

Various pipe arrangements may be used depending on the layout of the building. One-pipe or two-pipe circuits may be used. The one-pipe system saves labour and material and is therefore cheaper; it is also neater and saves on duct space. The two-pipe system permits the pressure from the pump to act through the heat emitters and therefore any type of heat emitter may be installed; it also provides a quicker heat recovery and there is a reduction in the temperature differences in the heat emitters which makes regulation easier.

The diagrams show the various types of circuits:

(a) One-pipe ring—suitable for low-rise buildings. All the other circuits may be used in buildings two storeys in height or over.

(b) One-pipe ladder—suitable when it is possible to run horizontal pipes across the ceiling joists or inside a floor duct.

(c) One-pipe drop—may be used where it is possible to run vertical pipes in ducts or chases and make connections, by means of horizontal branch pipes, to the heat emitters. The system has the advantage of making the heat emitters self-venting.

(d) One-pipe parallel—may be used when the horizontal flow pipe is exposed in the room but the horizontal return pipe is housed in the ceiling void or a floor duct.

(e) Two-pipe parallel—may be used when both the horizontal flow and return pipes are housed in the ceiling void or a floor duct.

(f) Two-pipe reverse return—often called the equal travel system because the lengths of pipe run from the boiler to each heat emitter are the same. Note that the length of the circuit for emitter A is the same as that for emitter B. The system provides a well balanced circuit.

(g) Two-pipe upfeed—may be used when the horizontal flow and return mains can be installed in a floor or wall duct on the ground floor. It is useful when it is necessary to avoid long horizontal pipe runs above the ground floor.

79

Two-pipe high level return—used when it is impractical to install long horizontal flow and return pipes at ground floor level. The system is useful when installing heating in existing buildings having a solid ground floor.

Two-pipe drop—suitable when it is possible to install a main horizontal flow pipe at high level and a main horizontal return pipe at low level. It has the advantage of the one-pipe drop in making the heat emitters self-venting.

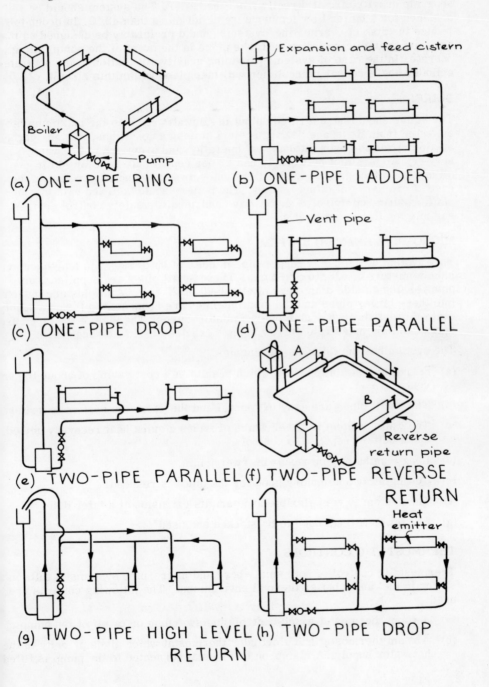

(a) ONE-PIPE RING

(b) ONE-PIPE LADDER

(c) ONE-PIPE DROP

(d) ONE-PIPE PARALLEL

(e) TWO-PIPE PARALLEL

(f) TWO-PIPE REVERSE RETURN

(g) TWO-PIPE HIGH LEVEL RETURN

(h) TWO-PIPE DROP

Domestic Heating Systems

SMALL-BORE SYSTEM

This system consists of 13 or 19 mm bore pipe circuits in which the hot wat is forced by a pump. The primary circuit to the hot water indirect cylinder may be connected to the pumped heating circuit, or alternatively it may be a separate gravity circuit directly from the boiler. The system should be designed for a boiler flow temperature of not more than 82 °C. In order to reduce the risk of overheating, systems should preferably be designed so tha adequate gravity circulation will take place in the event of the pump failing t operate. In the case of systems providing gravity circulation to the hot wate cylinder, the necessary circulation will take place within this circuit.

BOILERS

The boiler should have a rated output in kilowatts equal to the maximum hea emission from the space heating system at design conditions, plus an appro- priate margin to cover intermittent operation and provision of hot water service. A margin of between 10 and 20 per cent should be allowed for gas, oil and solid fuel gravity feed boilers and between 20 and 30 per cent in the case of ordinary solid fuel boilers. The boiler should be fitted with thermo- static control, safety valve, drain valve and adequate safety control devices suitable for the type of fuel used.

MICRO-PIPE HEATING SYSTEM

This system utilises soft copper pipe in coils of up to 200 m in length and ou side diameters of 6, 8, 10 or 12 mm. These small pipes are supplied from pipes having outside diameters of either 28 or 22 mm. Manifolds are inserte into these larger pipes and the smaller pipes are connected to them to suppl heat emitters through double entry radiator valves. The size of the pipes use depends on the mass rate of flow in kg/s required to flow through them.

The system has the following advantages

(a) Saving in installation time, which results in a cost saving of about 15 per cent.

(b) The small pipes are easy to conceal and therefore the system is neater.

(c) The water content is lower which provides a quick heat recovery period and a better response to controls.

(d) Long lengths of pipe result in fewer joints.

(e) Cutting away and making good for the pipes is reduced.

(f) The system is very flexible and permits extension at a later date.

(g) Far fewer fittings need to be stocked and used.

THERMOSTATIC CONTROLS

Thermostatic control of both small-bore and micro-pipe systems results in saving in fuel and a better thermal environment. The following controls are used:

(a) A room thermostat which controls the switching on or off of the pump.

(b) A room thermostat and a cylinder thermostat which gives priority to the hot water supply. A clamp-on thermostat connected to the pump is fitted

81

to the hot water cylinder. Heating is normally controlled by the room thermostat which switches the pump on or off. Whenever the cylinder water temperature falls below the setting of the clamp-on thermostat, the room thermostat is overridden and the pump is switched off. The boiler then heats the water up to the required temperature and the clamp-on thermostat then switches on the pump allowing the heating to be resumed. Fuel economy is achieved because the clamp-on thermostat can be set at a lower temperature than the boiler thermostat.

) Zone control by means of thermostatic valves inserted in the main flow pipe to each zone, e.g. in a house one valve can control the bedrooms and another the rooms downstairs.

) Three-way thermostatic mixing valve connected between the main flow and return pipes and operated by a room thermostat. When the room reaches the required temperature, the thermostat operates the valve and permits cooler water in the return pipe to mix with the hotter water in the flow pipe.

) Thermostatic radiator valves on each radiator provide the best result, because each room is under individual temperature control. The temperature of the water in the calorifier is controlled by a thermostatic valve inserted in the primary circuit.

igures 1 and 2 show both a small-bore and a micro-pipe system for a three-
·droomed house. The small-bore system is an 'open' type with gravity
rculation to the calorifier. The micro-pipe system is a 'sealed' system
ith pumped circulation to the calorifier.

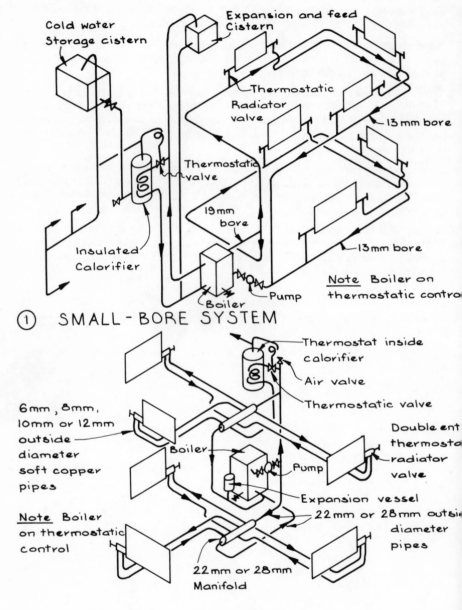

Cold water
Storage cistern

Expansion and feed
Cistern

Thermostatic
Radiator
valve

13 mm bore

Thermostatic
valve

19mm
bore

13mm bore

Insulated
Calorifier

Boiler

Pump

Note Boiler on
thermostatic control

① SMALL-BORE SYSTEM

Thermostat inside
calorifier

Air valve

Thermostatic valve

6mm, 8mm,
10mm or 12mm
outside
diameter
soft copper
pipes

Boiler

Pump

Double ent
thermosta
radiator
valve

Note Boiler
on thermostatic
control

Expansion vessel

22mm or 28mm outsi
diameter
pipes

22mm or 28mm
Manifold

② MICRO - PIPE SYSTEM

DOMESTIC HEATING SYSTEMS

the absence of sufficient warmth from internal heat gains from the Sun,
ghting, people and machinery, the heat losses from the body must be balanced
· the installation of heat emitters.

ne normal heat losses from the body are approximately

Radiation   45 per cent

Convection   30 per cent

Evaporation   25 per cent

ne main types of heat emitter used for hot water heating systems are as
·llows

ADIATORS, fig. 1

hese may be column, hospital or panel types, made from steel or cast iron.
eel radiators are made from light gauge steel pressings welded together;
ey are used extensively for heating systems in domestic buildings. Cast
on radiators are bulkier and heavier, but will stand up to rough use in
hools, colleges, hospitals and factories.

a radiator is fitted against a wall, staining of the wall above the radiator
ill occur due to convection currents picking up dust from the floor. To
event this, a shelf should be fitted about 76 mm above the radiator and the
elf should have a seal at the back, otherwise black stains will appear above
e shelf. End shields should be provided to the shelf to prevent black stains
the sides. Insulation behind a radiator will improve its efficiency.

osition of radiators   The best position is under a window, so that cold air
tering the room is heated by the radiator and thus prevents cold air passing
ong the floor, which would cause discomfort to the occupants of the room.

ADIANT PANELS, fig 2

hese are similar in appearance to panel radiators but are designed to trans-
it more heat by radiation. The surfaces are flat and a layer of insulation at
e back of the panel ensures that most of the heat passes out at the front. The
nels are very suitable for workshops and warehouses where the panels may
suspended between 3 and 4 m above the floor. Since most of the heat given
t by the panel is by radiation, the air temperature may be about 3 °C lower
an for convective heating and there is about 15 per cent saving in fuel costs.

ADIANT STRIPS, fig 3

hese are similar in construction to the radiant panel but are usually narrower
nd longer. Heating pipes up to 30 m long are fixed to an insulated metal plate
hich also becomes heated by conduction from the pipes. The strips are fixed
verhead in workshops or warehouses.

ATURAL CONVECTOR, fig. 4

hese can be cabinet or skirting types. The cabinet type has a finned heat
xchanger near the bottom and this heats the column of air above it, which
s displaced by the cooler air in the room. A damper is used to control the
ow of air through the cabinet. The skirting type also has a finned heat
xchanger near the bottom and operates on the same principle of the cabinet

type. If the floor is to be carpeted, care must be taken to ensure that a gap is left under the bottom of the heater casing or convection through the heater will be prevented.

FAN CONVECTORS, fig. 5

These have a finned heat exchanger usually fitted near the top of the cabinet. The fan or fans fitted below the heat exchanger draw air from the room which is then forced through the heat exchanger, where it is heated before being forced into the room. The fan or fans may have variable speeds and thermostatic control of the heat output from the convector may be by changing the fan speed.

Alternatively, each convector may be provided with a thermostatic valve on the flow pipe. The convector provides quick circulation of air in the room and air may be circulated during summer when the heating is off.

OVERHEAD UNIT HEATER, fig. 6

These are similar to the fan convector but are designed to be fixed overhead in workshops, garages and warehouses. They have the advantage of providing good air circulation and a clear wall area. If required, they may be provided with a duct to the outside so that fresh air may be drawn through them.

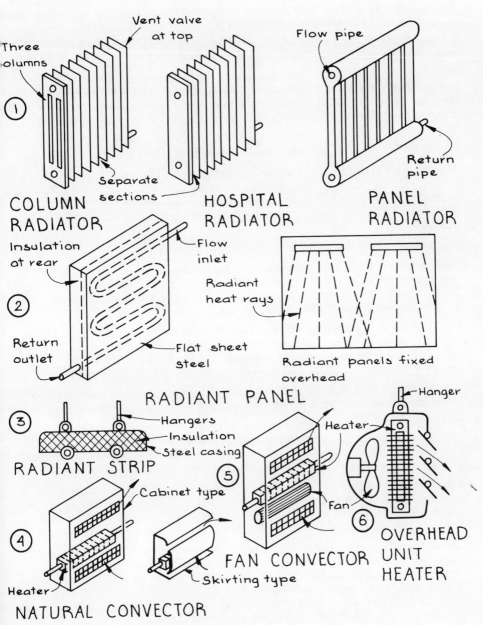

1 Three columns — Vent valve at top — Separate sections

COLUMN RADIATOR

HOSPITAL RADIATOR

Flow pipe — Return pipe

PANEL RADIATOR

2 Insulation at rear — Flow inlet — Return outlet — Flat sheet steel

Radiant heat rays — Radiant panels fixed overhead

RADIANT PANEL

3 Hangers — Insulation — Steel casing

RADIANT STRIP

4 Cabinet type — Heater — Skirting type

NATURAL CONVECTOR

5 Heater — Fan

FAN CONVECTOR

6 Hanger — Heater

OVERHEAD UNIT HEATER

HEAT EMITTERS

Water Mains

Large trunk mains are placed under the roadway whilst smaller branch mains are placed under the footpath. To avoid damage by heavy traffic or frost the pipes should be laid at least 914 mm below ground, preferably on firm ground or on a concrete foundation 150 mm thick.

A 'circulating main' is preferable to a 'dead leg' where stagnation of the water occurs and frequent flushing out is necessary.

Testing Before backfilling the trench the main should be tested by a force pump to twice the working pressure. When making the test it is necessary to strut the pipes and bends or the pipes may move under pressure and joints be broken. A good working pressure for mains is 552 kPa or approximately 55 m head.

Materials for pipes Cast Iron pipes. These may be vertically cast or spun.

Vertical cast iron pipes are made in lengths of 2·743 m and 3·658 m their diameters ranging from 38 mm to 1·219 m. Spun cast iron pipes are made in lengths of 3·658 m, 4·877 m and 5·486 m and in diameters ranging from 76 mm to 610 mm. The pipes usually have spigot and socket joints and are joined by caulked lead.

Fig. 1 shows a section through a spigot and socket joint.

Other methods of jointing. Mechanical joints may be used instead of caulked spigot and socket joints. Mechanical joints are very suitable for waterlogged ground or where settlement might occur. The joint will permit a slight amount of lineal expansion and deflection.

Fig. 2 shows a 'screwed gland' mechanical joint having a lead tipped rubber ring. The ring is compressed by screwing up the gland with a special key inserted in the notches. Graphite paste applied between the gland and joint ring and on the threads acts as a lubricant.

Fig. 3 shows a bolt type mechanical joint which has a rubber ring at the base of the socket secured by a pressure ring held and tightened in position by bolts

Steel pipes These are much stronger and lighter than cast iron pipes and are obtainable in larger lengths thus requiring fewer joints. For protecting the inside surface a bituminous lining is recommended. Fig. 4 shows a caulked lead spigot and socket joint on a mild steel pipe.

Asbestos cement pipes These are suitable for water that may corrode iron or steel pipes. If made thick enough they will withstand the same internal water pressure as cast iron pipes, but are brittle and more likely to fracture. Fig. 5 shows a compression coupling joint for asbestos cement pipes.

Connections to mains, Fig. 6 The main is tapped whilst under pressure from a special appliance. The appliance is attached to the main by chains and the chamber made water tight with a rubber washer. The hole is drilled and tapped and the top cover revolved so that the plug cock is brought directly over the hole into which it is screwed and tightened. The appliance is removed and the service pipe connected to the plug cock outlet.

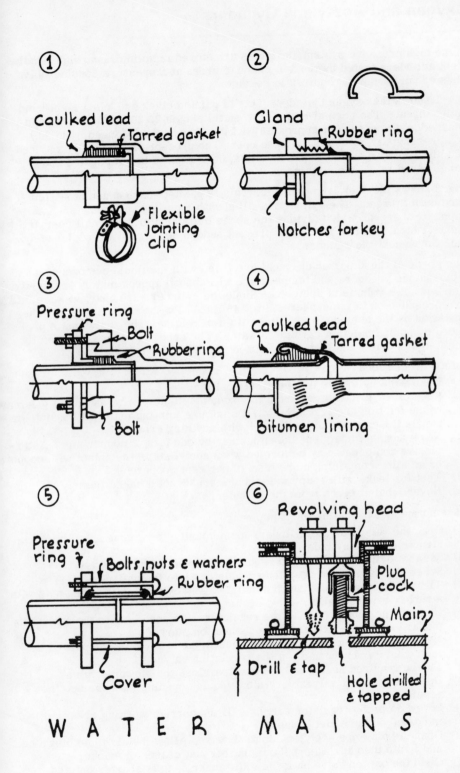

① Caulked lead — Tarred gasket — Flexible jointing clip

② Gland — Rubber ring — Notches for key

③ Pressure ring — Bolt — Rubber ring — Bolt

④ Caulked lead — Tarred gasket — Bitumen lining

⑤ Pressure ring — Bolts, nuts & washers — Rubber ring — Cover

⑥ Revolving head — Plug cock — Main — Drill & tap — Hole drilled & tapped

W A T E R   M A I N S

Oxygen and Acetylene Cylinders

In the high pressure system, the gases are stored in solid drawn, high tensile steel cylinders tested by the gas manufacturers at a pressure considerably higher than normally required in service.

Fig. 1 shows the oxygen cylinder. This is painted black and has a right hand outlet thread. The normal cylinder when full, holds 22.30 m^3 of oxygen and is charged to a pressure of approx 13789 kPa. Oxygen is produced by highly compressing air, producing intense cold. The pressure is gradually reduced and nitrogen evaporates first leaving liquid oxygen to be evaporated and compressed into a steel cylinder.

Fig. 2 shows the acetylene cylinder. This is painted maroon and has a left hand outlet thread. The cylinder is filled with a porous substance such as kapok or charcoal, which divides the space into innumerable small compartments, which, should a fire start, prevent sudden decomposition of the acetylene throughout the cylinder.

The pores of the kapok or charcoal are filled with the liquid acetone, which at atmospheric pressure and temperature will absorb approximately twenty-five times its own volume of acetylene. Since the cylinders are charged when full to a pressure of 15 atmospheres, i.e. 1551.329 kPa, the amount of acetylene absorbed by the acetone is 375 times its own volume. The acetylene is produced by adding calcium carbide to water. The crude acetylene is carefully purified and dried, and then compressed into the steel cylinder.

Safety Precautions
(a) Secure the cylinders in a vertical position.
(b) Keep oil or grease away from the oxygen cylinder. Any escape of gas may cause friction and ignite the oil. Do not use jointing material in joints or handle the cylinder or equipment with anything greasy.
(c) Never connect acetylene hose together by odd bits of copper pipe. An explosive compound may be formed when acetylene is in contact with copper, or an alloy containing more than 70 per cent copper.
(d) Test for leaks with soapy water and a brush, not a naked flame.
(e) Never inhale oxygen from the cylinder.

Assembling and Operating the Equipment
(a) Open the valves on the cylinders momentarily, to remove any dirt or obstruction in the cylinder valve.
(b) See that cylinder valves and regulators are not oily or greasy.
(c) Screw the oxygen and acetylene regulators into the cylinders.
(d) Tighten the regulators into the outlet valves by tapping the wing nuts with a rubber headed mallet.
(e) Connect the rubber hose to the regulators, the acetylene to the connection marked A and the oxygen to the connection marked O.
(f) Before connecting the torch to the hoses, the hoses must be purged by momentarily screwing down the regulating valves.
(g) Fit the required nozzle to the blowpipe; close the blowpipe valves.
(h) Open the cylinder valves very slowly; quick opening may damage the regulator.
(i) Screw down the regulator valves until the correct working pressure is indicated on the outlet gauge.
(j) Open the blowpipe acetylene control valve. Allow the air to be blown out and ignite the gas. Adjust flame until it just ceases to smoke.
(k) Open the oxygen valve until the white inner cone is sharply defined.

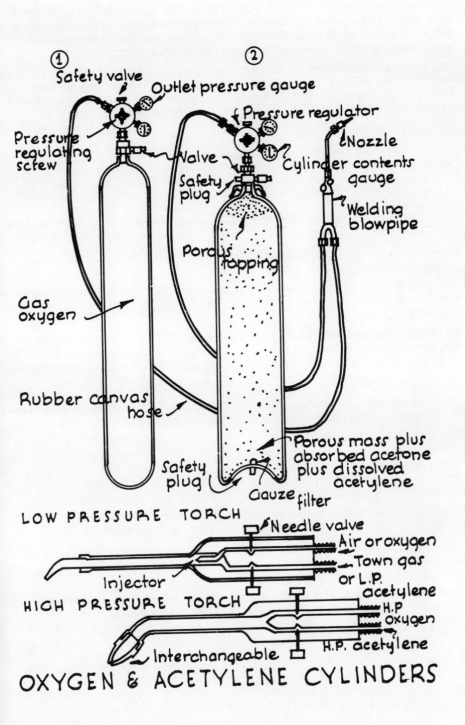

OXYGEN & ACETYLENE CYLINDERS

Lead Burning

Lead welding or lead burning is a method used to joint together lead pipe or lead sheet by the fusion of the lead. The process has been used for centuries and the Romans made their lead pipes by coiling sheet lead round a mandril and fusing the edges together by means of a red hot iron.

Due to the action of acids on solder, lead burning is used extensively by plumbers for work in chemical factories. In recent years however, the domestic plumber has taken advantage of lead burning, and it is now used extensively for joining lead pipe and sheet on building work.

Advantages of lead burning

(a) Cheaper and quicker than soldering or bossing.
(b) The molecules, being the same as the parent metal, expand and contract in equal ratio with the parent metal. With soldering there is unequal expansion and contraction and cracking of the lead often occurs near the seam.
(c) Lead burning can be adapted for ornamental work, e.g. rainwater heads and pipes.

The Technique Make certain that the correct nozzle and gas pressure are being used.

Stand or sit in a comfortable position and support the rubber hose pipes either over the shoulder or round the forearm to prevent 'dragging' of the pipes on the bench.

Hold the torch so as to obtain a good balance. This can be done by either holding the touch like a fountain pen or by holding it on the palm of the hand. The grip should be very light, and the fore finger and thumb should give full control

Use the white inner cone of the flame like the point of a pencil.

Acquire the correct rhythm of blowpipe and filler rod (if used), to produce successive molten pools which are allowed to solidify as the work proceeds.

'Bulk' burning The student can prove to himself the importance of applying the flame on the 'bulk' of the lead. Hold a piece of scrap lead with one hand and apply the flame to the centre of the sheet. It will be noticed that it takes about twice as long to burn a hole through the centre than through the edge of the sheet. This principle is applied to all lead burned joints on sheet lead.

Flat butted seam, Fig. 1 The two edges are 'burned' in so as to obtain one solid piece of lead before building up the seam by use of a filler rod.

Flat lapped seam, Fig. 2 The first loading is made on the underlying piece of lead, where the bulk of lead occurs. The edge of the overlap is carefully melted in with this first loading.

Inclined and upright, Figs. 3 and 4 A platform is made so that the flame can be applied to this bulk of lead. The overlapping edge is then melted down on to this platform.

91

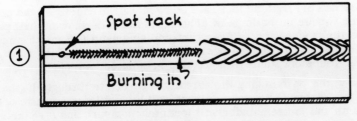

FLAT BURNED SEAM

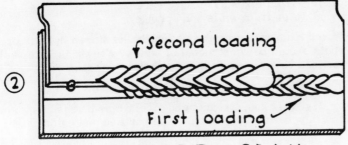

FLAT LAPPED SEAM

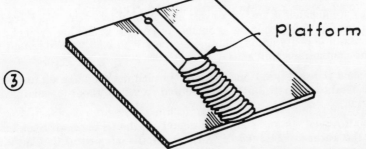

INCLINED SEAM - BUTTED

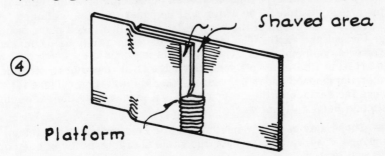

LEADBURNING

Sources of Water Supply

All water we use originates from rain, snow or hail produced by the condens tion of water vapour in the form of clouds. As the rain, snow or hail passes through the atmosphere it dissolves carbonic acid gas CO_2, and this increase its solvent power. Water charged with CO_2 will readily dissolve substances like chalk or limestone and will hold them in solution as bicarbonates.

Some of the water, on reaching the earth, will percolate through the ground a be held by the impervious stratum. Some will be lost by evaporation or be used by plants and the remainder will form lakes, rivers and streams.

The sources of supply will therefore be one of the following:
(a) rainwater—from roofs, paved areas etc;
(b) surface water—from lakes, rivers, streams;
(c) underground water from wells and springs.

Rainwater Water from roofs may be collected and stored in butts or storage tanks. The roofs should be constructed of slates or tiles, as water collected from thatch or lead covered roofs will be contaminated.

As rainwater is soft it is 'plumbo solvent', i.e. it dissolves lead.

Surface water, Fig.1 Lakes, streams and rivers may be used as a source of supply but it is imperative that the water be purified and chlorinated.

If natural sources are not available it is necessary to construct an impound-ing reservoir. Quite a number of towns and cities obtain their water supply in this way, Bradford, Halifax and Newport being examples.

The water impounded in the reservoir is obtained from drainage areas or tracts of land called gathering grounds. Moorland gathering ground produces water containing peaty acids, which dissolves lead easily. Filtering through limestone neutralises this acid.

Underground water, Figs.1 and 2 Underground sources are either wells or springs. Wells are artificially formed and may be either: (a) shallow, (b) dee (c) artesian.

(a) A shallow well is one sunk less deep than the first impervious stratum and the water is obtained from the water bearing subsoil. The water is normally soft and may be highly polluted.
(b) A deep well is the type sunk to the water bearing stratum below the first impervious stratum. The water will be purer than that obtained from a shallow well because of the natural filtration that takes place on its pass age through the earth. The water may be temporarily or permanently hard or a combination of the two.
(c) An artesian well is a well sunk below the first impervious stratum to water imprisoned under pressure. When the water is released it rises above the surface of the ground. The water may have the same characte istics of deep well water.

Springs These may be either intermittent or land springs, or artesian or main springs. The water may have the same characteristics of deep or artesian well water.

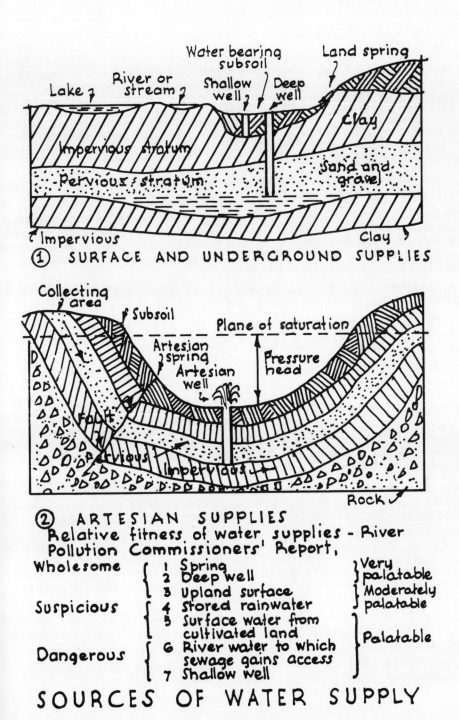

Water bearing subsoil

Land spring

Lake

River or stream

Shallow well

Deep well

Impervious stratum

Clay

Pervious stratum

Sand and gravel

Impervious

Clay

① SURFACE AND UNDERGROUND SUPPLIES

Collecting area

Subsoil

Plane of saturation

Artesian spring

Artesian well

Pressure head

Fault

Pervious

Impervious

Rock

② ARTESIAN SUPPLIES

Relative fitness of water supplies - River Pollution Commissioners' Report,

Wholesome	{	1	Spring	}	Very palatable
		2	Deep well		
	{	3	Upland surface	}	Moderately palatable
Suspicious	{	4	Stored rainwater		
	{	5	Surface water from cultivated land	}	Palatable
Dangerous	{	6	River water to which sewage gains access		
	{	7	Shallow well		

SOURCES OF WATER SUPPLY

Pumps

A pump is used to raise water to a higher level or to force water through pipework.

When it is used for raising water, its operation depends on the pressure of the atmosphere, which is about 101.33 kPa, or 10.33 m head of water. Theoretically a pump could lift water to a height of 10.33 m, but in practice, due to leakage from valves, etc., the height is about 7.60 m.

Jack lift pump, Fig. 1 This is the old village pump, and is the simplest type. Water is lifted to the outlet only and the height to which water can be delivered is limited to 7.60 m.

Action of pump. The handle is operated and causes the bucket to move up and down (reciprocate) inside the barrel.

On the first upward stroke the suction valve is opened and the bucket valve closed, causing air to be withdrawn from the barrel and a partial vacuum to be created below the bucket. Immediately this partial vacuum is formed the greater pressure of the atmosphere acting on the water in the well pushes water up the suction pipe and into the barrel.

On the first downward stroke the suction valve is closed and the bucket valve opened allowing the bucket to pass freely through the water.

On the second upward stroke the suction valve is opened and the bucket valve closed. The water above the bucket is therefore ejected from the barrel through the spout.

Water will continue to be ejected from the pump by the up and down movement of the bucket until sufficient water has been withdrawn.

Fig. 2 shows a section through a centrifugal pump which is used extensively for heating systems, drainage and hot and cold water systems.

Lift pump, Fig. 3 Action of pump. Exactly the same sequence of operations is passed through as described in the Jack pump but the water in this pump is lifted up the delivery pipe instead of through the spout.

The air in the chamber acts as a cushion to absorb shock, and maintains a steady flow of water. The air is compressed and then by virtue of its elasticity lifts water up the delivery pipe during the downward stroke of the bucket.

Lift and force pump, Fig. 4 Action of pump. On the first downward stroke air is forced out of the barrel or cylinder leaving behind a partial vacuum.

On the first upward stroke water is forced into the barrel by the atmospheric pressure acting upon the water in the well. Air is prevented from entering the barrel because of the closed delivery valve.

On the second downward stroke the water in the barrel is forced into the air chamber and up the delivery pipe. The air in the chamber, being compressed, absorbs the shock.

On the second upward stroke the compressed air forces more water up the delivery pipe thus maintaining a steady flow of water.

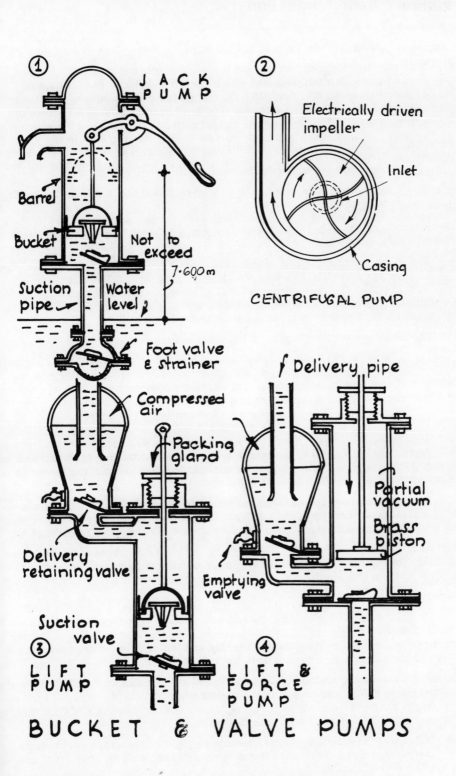

① JACK PUMP

Barrel

Bucket

Suction pipe

Water level

Not to exceed 7·600 m

② Electrically driven impeller

Inlet

Casing

CENTRIFUGAL PUMP

Foot valve & strainer

Compressed air

Packing gland

Delivery pipe

Partial vacuum

Brass piston

Delivery retaining valve

Emptying valve

Suction valve

③ LIFT PUMP

④ LIFT & FORCE PUMP

BUCKET & VALVE PUMPS

Sanitary Accommodation

The Building Regulations Part P.3.1976 state

(1) 'Sanitary accommodation' means a room or space constructed for use in connection with a building and which contains water closet fittings or urinal fittings, whether or not it also contains other sanitary or lavatory fittings: Provided that if any such room or space contains a cubicle or cubicles so constructed as to allow free circulation of air throughout the room or space; this regulation shall be treated as applying to the room a a whole and not to the cubicle or cubicles separately.

(2) No sanitary accommodation shall open directly into:-

(a) a habitable room, unless the room is used solely for sleeping or dre purposes; or

(b) a room used for a kitchen or scullery purposes; or

(c) a room in which any person is habitually employed in manufacture, t or business.

Fig 1. shows that method of entering a W.C. cubicle from a workroom or kitchen via a ventilated lobby, which would satisfy the Regulations.
Fig 2. shows the method of ventilating several cubicles by means of a lo lantern light. To calculate the size of opening for ventilation the total flo area of the room must be taken into account.

(3) Sanitary accommodation shall have either:-

(a) a window, skylight or other similar means of ventilation which opens directly into the external air and of which the area capable of being is not less than one-twentieth of the floor area: or

(b) mechanical means of ventilation which effects not less than three air changes per hour and discharges directly into the external air.

Fig 3. shows W.C.s. and urinals fixed in a basement and fig 4, W.C. cubic with no external wall. It will be necessary in both cases to provide mech ventilation by means of an extraction duct and fan to give the apartments 3 air changes per hour. Some Authorities require the fan and motor to be duplicate with automatic switch over.

(4) Any sanitary accommodation which includes a W.C. and which can be entered directly from a room used for sleeping or dressing purposes be so constructed that it can be entered without passing through any room, but this paragraph shall not apply if:-

(a) (in the case of a dwelling) there is other such sanitary accommodati within the dwelling which can be entered without passing through any such room: or

(b) (in the case of a private dwelling house) there is other such sanitary accommodation outside such house which is used exclusively with su house; or

(c) (in any other case) there is within the building other such sanitary ac modation which is available for common use.

Fig 5 shows the method of entering a bathroom containing a W.C. when the is another W.C. either within the dwelling (a) or outside the dwelling (b).
Fig 6 shows the method of entering a bathroom containing a W.C. when the no other W.C. outside or within the building.

Note. The Regulations do not mention lighting of sanitary apartments. It means therefore that where there is no external wall an apartment may be lighted artificially.

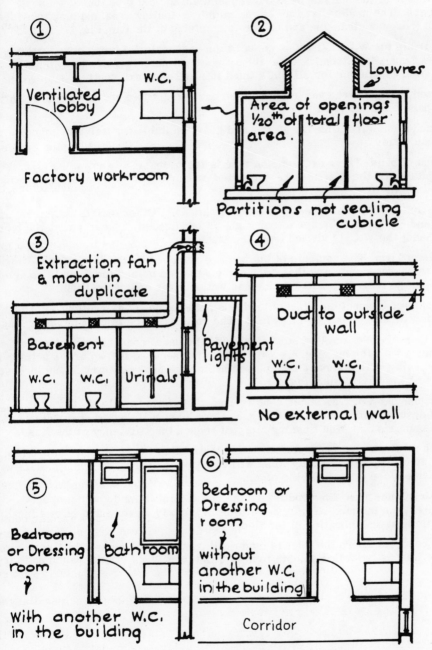

① Ventilated lobby — W.C. — Factory workroom

② Louvres — Area of openings 1/20th of total floor area. — Partitions not sealing cubicle

③ Extraction fan & motor in duplicate — Basement — W.C. — W.C. — Urinals — Pavement lights

④ Duct to outside wall — W.C. — W.C. — No external wall

⑤ Bedroom or Dressing room — Bathroom — With another W.C. in the building

⑥ Bedroom or Dressing room — without another W.C. in the building — Corridor

SANITARY ACCOMMODATION

Wash-down Water Closets

The shape of the pan has been developed from the old type long and short hoppers. The modern type gives the minimum fouling area and also provides for a thorough cleansing and complete emptying of the pan, Fig. 1.

Materials for W.Cs Vitreous china is the best material being non-porous throughout, very strong, and durable; it does not discolour or stain. The material is suitable for all W.Cs fixed internally or externally.

Glazed earthenware pans are not as strong and durable and are suitable only for pans fixed internally.

Glazed stoneware pans are strong and heavy; suitable for fixing in schools and factories.

Types of pans The most common type is the pedestal as shown in Fig. 1. For hospitals etc. the W.C. may be supported by cantilever or a corbel, thus provid- ing a clear floor space for easy cleaning.

Pan Outlet The main types are S and straight P. Other outlets obtainable are 45° and 90° turned P traps either right or left handed. To determine the type of 'hand' the W.C. is viewed from the front.

Action of pan The contents of the pan are removed by the force and volume of the flush water entering the pan and are removed before the flush is complete. The pan is therefore filled with clean water at the end of the flush.

Flush pipe connection When a lead flush pipe is used an excellent joint is made with an octopus collar, Fig. 2. The collar may be of cast or sheet lead.

For porcelain-enamelled steel flush pipe the usual connection consists of either a rubber ring, Fig. 3, or a brass collar secured by two brass bolts to a brass ring, with a rubber ring placed behind the brass collar and compressed against the W.C. collar, Fig. 4.

For cheaper work, a rubber cone is used. The cone is filled with red lead putty and secured with copper wire, Fig. 5. Care must be taken to ensure that putty does not pass into the flushing rim and reduce the efficiency of the flush.

With all flush pipe connections it is essential that the flush pipe enters the collar centrally or a faulty flush will result—one side of the flushing rim will receive more water than the other.

Outlet Connection On wood floors the outlet joint is made with a special rubber jointing ring. This type of joint is slightly flexible and allows for settlement and vibration of the floor, Fig. 6.

On concrete floors the joint is made with gasket and 1 cement to 1 sand mortar. The joint is trowelled smooth to a 45° fillet, Fig. 7.

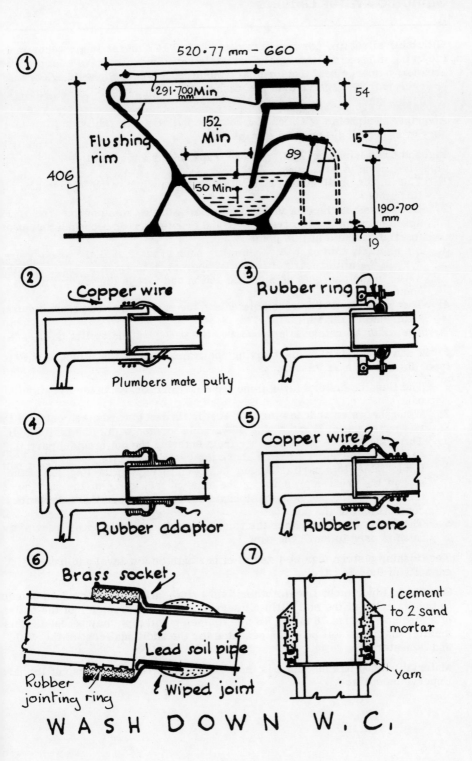

① 520·77 mm - 660

291·700 Min
mm

54

152 Min

15°

Flushing rim

89

406

50 Min

190·700 mm

19

② Copper wire

Plumbers mate putty

③ Rubber ring

④ Rubber adaptor

⑤ Copper wire

Rubber cone

⑥ Brass socket

Lead soil pipe

Rubber jointing ring

Wiped joint

⑦ I cement to 2 sand mortar

Yarn

WASH DOWN W.C.

Siphonic Water Closets

With their silent and positive action, siphonic W.Cs are strongly recommend for fixing in houses, flats, hotels, hospitals etc. They also have a larger wat area and a deeper seal than ordinary wash-down types. Siphonic W.Cs are, however, more expensive than the wash-down type and do not stand up as we to rough usage.

A variety of siphonic W.Cs can be obtained but all types fall within the cate gory of either single or double traps.

Fig. 1 shows a siphonic W.C. with two traps, and is known as the 'exhaust ac type. Its action is as follows:
1. The flushing cistern lever is pulled down, causing water to pass down th flush pipe.
2. Water passing the end of the air pipe at A draws some of the air from t space between the two traps at B, and creates a reduction in air pressu (partial vacuum) at this point.
3. Immediately this partial vacuum has been created at B, the greater pres sure of the atmosphere 101.33 kPa approx., acting on the surface of the water in the pan, sets up siphonic action and forces the water with its contents out of the pan.
4. This siphonic action is completed and the pan is emptied before the flus water enters the pan.
   The water therefore simply washes the pan down and refills the first se

Fig. 2 shows a siphonic closet having one trap known as the 'Bulbous outlet' type. Its action is as follows:

1. The flushing cistern lever is pulled down and causes water to enter the pan.
2. When the water reaches the bulb A it is thrown towards the centre of th restricted outlet B and a plug of water is formed within the outlet at B.
3. This plug of water prevents air from entering the outlet and a partial vacuum is therefore created above the restricted outlet.
4. Immediately this partial vacuum has been formed in the long leg of the siphon, the greater pressure of the atmosphere, acting on the surface of the water in the pan sets up siphonic action and forces the water, with it contents, out of the pan.
5. The pan is emptied before the flush is finished, and the latter part of the flush is used to refill the pan.

The flushing cistern may be fixed at either high or low level and have a capacity of 9 or 14 litre.

Soil Stack Since most Local Authorities' bylaws allow a soil stack to be equ to the diameter of the soil fitting it serves, and as the diameter of the outlet of a siphonic W.C. is 76 mm, a 76 mm diameter soil pipe may be used. This smaller diameter soil pipe compensates for the additional cost of the W.C. and is neater.

Material used Vitreous china is the best material to use because of its hard impervious surface.

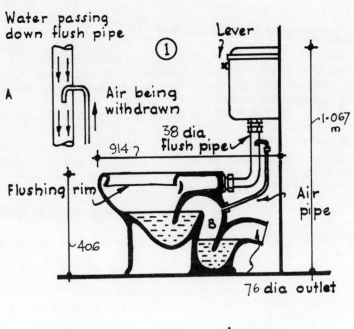

Water passing down flush pipe

A

① Lever

Air being withdrawn

38 dia flush pipe

1·067 m

914

Flushing rim

406

Air pipe

B

76 dia outlet

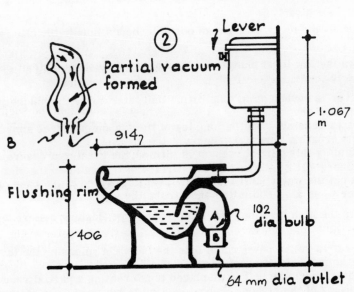

② Lever

Partial vacuum formed

B

914

1·067 m

Flushing rim

406

A

102 dia bulb

64 mm dia outlet

SIPHONIC WATER CLOSETS

Water Waste Preventors

Modern types of flushing cisterns are known as water waste preventors because water under normal conditions cannot enter the flush pipe other than siphonic action.

There are two main types of cisterns, namely plunger and bell, the former i often called the 'Japkap' type, and the latter the 'Burlington' type. Both type work on the principle of the siphon. Cisterns are made of cast iron, porcela enamelled cast iron, glazed fireclay or stoneware, vitreous china, pressed steel, plastic, aluminium alloy, copper, or wood lead lined. When choosing a flushing cistern, appearance, silence in action and sturdiness are factors to considered. The Bell type is noisy but sturdy and is suitable for factories e The water regulations of local authorites vary in their requirements for the capacity of the cistern which may be 9 or 14 litre.

Fixing of cisterns Cisterns may be fixed at either high or low level. The hi level position is the more efficient, but when cisterns are fixed in bathroom etc, the low level position is preferable because of its neater appearance.

For high level positions the base of the cistern should be fixed 1.524 m abo the pan outlet so as to ensure a good flush.

The plunger cistern may be used for either high or low level position but the bell type is used in the high level position only.

Flush Pipe Because of the greater head available above the W.C. pan, the hi level cistern requires a flush pipe of only 32 mm diameter but to compensat for the loss of head the low level cistern requires 38 mm or 50 mm diamete flush pipe.

A flush pipe should be as straight as possible; bends impair the efficiency of the flush.

Fig. 1 shows the low level plunger or 'Japkap' type flushing cistern which operates as follows:

(a) The lever is pushed down thus lifting the water above the plunger over the crown of the siphon.
(b) The water passing down the long leg of the siphon displaces some of the air thus creating a partial vacuum at the crown.
(c) Immediately this partial vacuum is formed, the greater pressure of the atmosphere 101 kPa acting on the surface of the water in the cistern, forces out the water until the water level is lowered to the base of the cylinder when air is admitted and breaks the siphonic action.

Fig. 2 shows the high level bell or 'Burlington' type flushing cistern with the following action:

(a) The lever is pulled down which lifts the bell. On releasing the lever the bell falls under its own weight.
(b) The water under the bell is displaced thus creating a partial vacuum in the long leg of the siphon. Siphonic action is set up and the atmospheric pressure forces the water out of the cistern until the water level is low ed to the base of the bell when air is admitted and breaks the siphonic action.

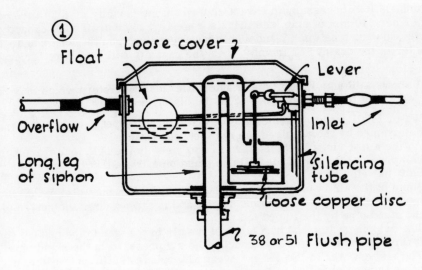

① PLUNGER TYPE

Float

Loose cover

Lever

Overflow

Inlet

Long leg of siphon

Silencing tube

Loose copper disc

38 or 51 Flush pipe

PLUNGER TYPE

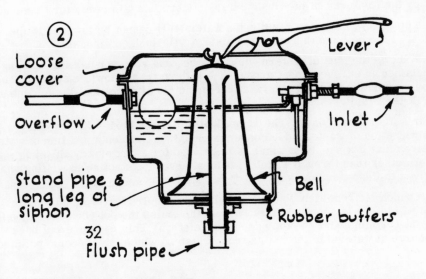

②

Loose cover

Lever

Overflow

Inlet

Stand pipe & long leg of siphon

Bell

Rubber buffers

32 Flush pipe

BELL TYPE

WATER WASTE PREVENTORS

Automatic Flushing Cisterns

Automatic flushing cisterns are used for flushing either urinals, drains or a range of W.Cs used by infants.

For urinals it is necessary to have a cistern with a capacity of 4.54 litre per stall or per 610 mm of slab (see urinals, page 107). For drains the capacity the cistern varies between 9 and 364 litres depending upon the length and diameter of the drain. For infants' W.Cs the capacity will be 9 litre for every W.C.

Fig. 1 shows a 'Roger Field' type of automatic flushing cistern which may be used for any of the above purposes, and the cistern works as follows:

(a) Water is allowed to dribble into the cistern via the pet cock at a rate determined by the required interval between flushes.

(b) As the water rises in the cistern it also rises in the bell, thus trapping and compressing the air in the bell and stand pipe. Note that the trap must be filled with water.

(c) Some of the air is forced through the trap, and when the water reaches the top of the stand pipe it trickles over it and is thrown down the centre of the stand pipe by the lipped top.

(d) The dripping water absorbs some of the air in the stand pipe and carries it through the trap, thereby reducing the air pressure in the stand pipe.

(e) The rising water in the cistern eventually creates sufficient head to over come the compression in the stand pipe and the water then rushes down the stand pipe setting up a siphonic action which empties the cistern until air is drawn below the bell and breaks the siphonage. The trap is re-set by the final part of the flush and the cistern is again ready for flushing.

If the cistern is filled too rapidly, the water level cannot be lowered to the bottom of the bell and therefore the cistern will flush continuously.

Fig. 2 shows the type of cistern which has become very popular for flushing urinals because it has a neat appearance with no trap below the cistern. The trap is inside the cistern, otherwise the principle of operation is the same as the 'Roger Field'.

Water Authorities Bylaws The Model Water Bylaws, Series XXV dealing with the prevention of waste, undue consumption, misuse or contamination of water requires that if a supply of water is to be used for an automatic flushing cistern other than through a meter, at least seven days notice in writing shall be given to the water company before installation.

The London Metropolitan Water Board bylaws require that if an automatic flushing cistern is supplied directly from the mains the pet cock should be fix at least 152 mm above the top edge of the cistern. This is to prevent back siphonage of water into the mains from a cistern which may become polluted.

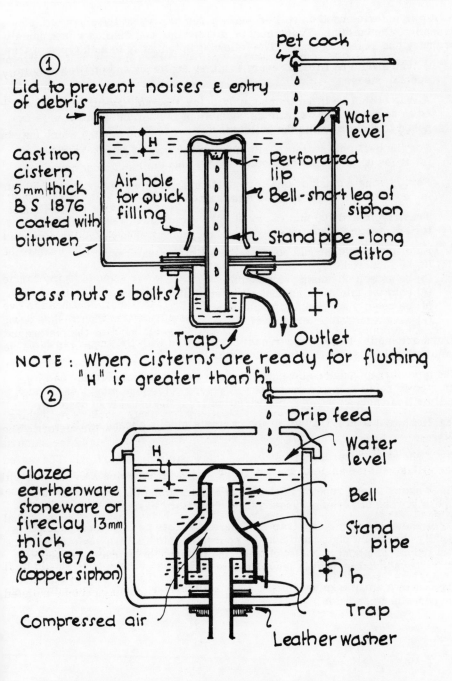

① Pet cock

Lid to prevent noises ε entry
of debris

Water level

Cast iron
cistern
5mm thick
B S 1876
coated with
bitumen

Air hole
for quick
filling

H

Perforated
lip

Bell - short leg of
siphon

Stand pipe - long
ditto

Brass nuts ε bolts?

h

Trap   Outlet

NOTE : When cisterns are ready for flushing
"H" is greater than "h"

② Drip feed

Water
level

Glazed
earthenware
stoneware or
fireclay 13mm
thick
B S 1876
(copper siphon)

H

Bell

Stand
pipe

h

Trap

Compressed air

Leather washer

AUTOMATIC FLUSHING CISTERNS

Traps

A trap is a device used on soil or waste pipes to prevent the entry of foul gases into the building. Traps may be divided into two distinct types, namely ordinary and resealing traps. The following notes apply to both types of trap.

1. A trap should be fitted to every sanitary appliance and omitted only in special cases.

2. A trap should be fitted immediately below the sanitary fitting it is requir ed to serve, so that as little as possible of the soil or waste pipe is exposed to the air inside the building.

3. For the dual pipe system a minimum water seal of 38 mm is required for traps up to 64 mm diameter.

4. For the single stack or one-pipe system a minimum water seal of 76 mm is required for traps up to 64 mm diameter.

5. Traps of 76 and 100 mm dia must have a minimum water seal of 50 mm for any system of plumbing.

6. An efficient trap should possess the following features:
    (a) be incorrodible;
    (b) be as self-cleansing as possible;
    (c) hold the minimum amount of water whilst giving the required seal;
    (d) be readily accessible for cleaning;
    (e) have a smooth internal surface.

Traps are made of lead, copper, cast iron (coated with Dr Angus Smith's solution), galvanised mild steel, plastic or brass.

The type of trap required depends upon the type of sanitary fitting and its position in relation to the waste or soil pipe, e.g. the pipe may pass through a wall or floor necessitating some variation from the usual trap position.

Fig. 1 shows a lead P trap used when a waste pipe is arranged with a slight fall.

Fig. 2 shows a copper S trap used when the waste pipe is vertical. The dotted lines illustrate the angle of the outlet for a ½ S or Q trap.

Fig. 3 shows a lead running trap used at a point along the 'run' of the waste pipe, e.g. when one trap serves a range of lavatory basins.

Fig. 4 shows a brass bottle trap used because of its better appearance. It is usually chromium plated and may be converted into an S trap by means of a bent union. The trap is easily cleaned and is ideal for hairdressing saloons where occasional stoppages may occur.

Fig. 5 shows a bag trap used instead of an S trap where space is limited, e.g. for pedestal wash basin.

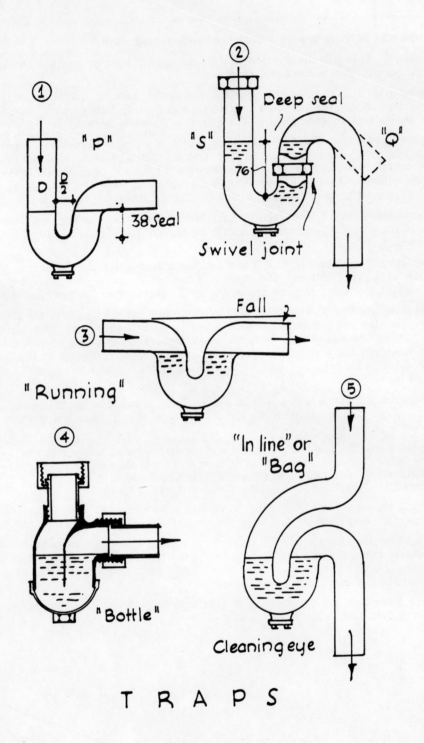

T R A P S

Unsealing of Traps

Traps may become unsealed in one of the following ways:

Leakage. This will allow water in the trap to empty on to the floor and is consequently soon noticed and repaired.

Siphonage. This may be either self siphonage or induced siphonage. Self siphonage, Fig. 1, occurs when a waste pipe is flowing full bore and, because of the absence of an antisiphon pipe, the trap becomes unsealed.

Induced siphonage, Fig. 2, occurs when two or more waste pipes are connnected together. The water from the farther sanitary fitting, flowing past the branch connection of the nearer fitting, withdraws air from the branch pipe of the nearer fitting. A partial vacuum is thus created on the outlet side of the trap of the nearer fitting and siphonic action is created, emptying the trap.

Compression Fig. 3 When the water is discharged from the higher fitting the air in the vertical pipe may become compressed sufficiently to 'blow' out the seal in the lower fitting.

Capillary Attraction Fig 4 If a piece of absorbent material is caught in the outlet of the trap with one end dipping in the water and the other hanging over the outlet, the water may be drawn out by capillarity through the material.

Wavering out Fig. 5 This is caused by gusts of wind passing over the top of the vent pipe and is often noticed in a W.C. trap on a windy day. The wind withdraws some of the air from the stack, thus creating a partial vacuum on the outlet side of the trap, and setting up siphonic action. The gusts of wind cause the water in the trap to sway backwards and forwards until the seal of the trap is broken.

Evaporation. If the trap is not in use, the rate of evaporation of the water will depend upon the humidity of the air in the room. The rate is approximately 2.5 mm per week.

Momentum. This is caused by the sudden discharge of water into the trap. The force of the water may be sufficient to unseal the trap. The discharge of a pail full of water into a W.C. is the most usual cause.

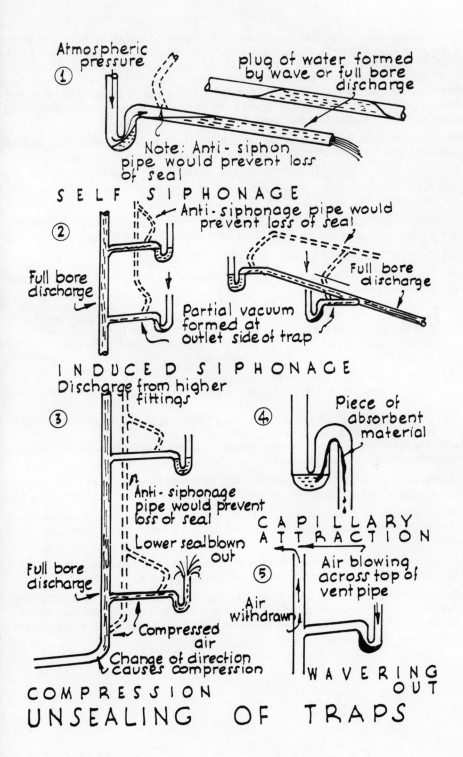

① Atmospheric pressure

plug of water formed by wave or full bore discharge

Note: Anti-siphon pipe would prevent loss of seal

S E L F   S I P H O N A G E

② Anti-siphonage pipe would prevent loss of seal

Full bore discharge

Full bore discharge

Partial vacuum formed at outlet side of trap

I N D U C E D   S I P H O N A G E

③ Discharge from higher fittings

Anti-siphonage pipe would prevent loss of seal

Full bore discharge

Lower seal blown out

Compressed air

Change of direction causes compression

C O M P R E S S I O N

④ Piece of absorbent material

C A P I L L A R Y   A T T R A C T I O N

⑤ Air withdrawn

Air blowing across top of vent pipe

W A V E R I N G   O U T

UNSEALING   OF   TRAPS

Resealing Traps

The purpose of an anti-siphon or resealing trap is to maintain the water seal of the trap without the installation of trap ventilating or anti-siphon pipes. The sanitary installation therefore, is simple and neat, but a thorough venting of the waste or soil pipe is not provided, which on long runs of pipe is a disadvantage that must be considered. With all types of anti-siphon or resealing traps the method of preserving the water seal is accomplished by means of a reserve chamber or reservoir forming part of the trap.

Water is retained in this chamber or reservoir during siphonage and empties back into the U of the trap when siphonage is finished.

The term anti-siphon therefore, is rather misleading as the trap does not prevent siphonic action from taking place, but preserves the seal of the trap under siphonic conditions.

The traps may be obtained from 51 mm to 76 mm internal diameters and with either P or S outlets for connecting to lead, copper or mild steel waste pipes.

Fig.1 shows the 'Grevak' trap. This works as follows:

(a) Siphonage of water in the trap takes place and the water level lowered to point A of the air pipe.
(b) Air then rushes through the air pipe B and equalises the air pressures on the inlet and outlet sides of the trap thus breaking the siphonic action.
(c) The air pressure acting on the surface of the water in the reserve chamber C causes water to be retained in the chamber which empties back into the U of the trap and maintains the seal.

Fig. 2 shows the 'McAlpine' trap. This works as follows:
(a) Siphonage of the water in the trap takes place and the water level is lower to point A.
(b) Air then rushes through the trap thus breaking the siphon and causing wat to be retained in the reserve chamber B.
(c) The water retained in the air chamber empties back into the U of the trap and maintains the seal.

Other makes of traps are obtainable, and although they differ in construction the principle of resealing the trap by means of a reserve chamber is the same

The criticism of resealing traps is that a current of fresh air does not flow through the waste pipe as in the case of ordinary traps which are trap ventilated.

In the case of drains, soil or waste pipes that are ventilated, the foul gases are removed and a better sanitary installation results.

The current of fresh air also keeps the insides of the pipes clean. The foul matter that may adhere to the sides of the pipes is dried by the current of fresh air and flakes off. This foul matter is then washed out leaving the inside of the pipe clean.

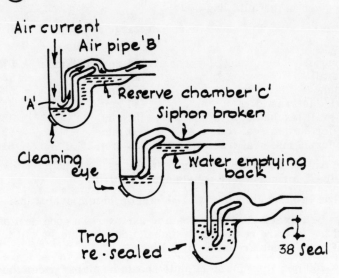

①

Air current
Air pipe 'B'
'A'
Reserve chamber 'C'
Siphon broken
Cleaning eye
Water emptying back
Trap re-sealed
38 Seal

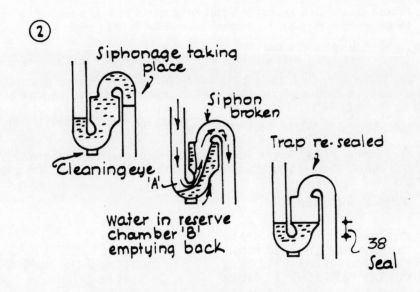

②

Siphonage taking place
Siphon broken
Cleaning eye
'A'
Trap re-sealed
Water in reserve chamber 'B' emptying back
38 Seal

RESEALING TRAPS

Baths and Lavatory Basins

Baths may be made from: porcelained enamelled, cast iron, sheet steel, fire-clay, Perspex and glass reinforced plastics.

Cast iron is the most popular material. B.S.1189:1972 gives two patterns: (a) rectangular (magna) in two sizes, and (b) tub (parallel) in one size, whose dimensions are given in the following table:

Dimensions	Rectangular (Magna)	Tub (parallel)
Length overall	1.676 m—1.828 m	1.676 m
Width overall	711 mm	737 mm
Width inside	578 mm	584 mm
Depth inside (at waste)	444 mm	432 mm
Height overall (excluding feed)	457 mm	435 mm
With feet for 38 mm seal trap	584 mm	597 mm
With feet for 76 mm seal trap	623 mm	610 mm

There are two patterns of feet: (a) adjustable, for use on a bath enclosed by a panel, and (b) fixed, for use where panels are not fitted.

Each pattern has two sizes for use with 38 mm or 76 mm seal traps.

Fixing It must be remembered that a bath in use exerts a good deal of force the feet, and if the feet are resting on a timber floor settlement will take pla unless special precautions are taken, as follows:

(a) 100 mm × 100 mm × 6 mm steel plate should be placed under the feet so as to distribute the load.

(b) If the bath is fixed against the wall, a 50 mm × 25 mm wood batten shoul be screwed to the wall for the top edge of the bath to rest on.

Fig. 1 shows the plan of a tub bath.
Fig. 2 shows elevation, plan and side view of a rectangular bath and ways of connecting hot and cold supplies, waste and overflow.

Some water authorities permit the overflow pipe to connect to the base of the trap as shown in Fig. 3. This method prevents the possibility of cold draught passing through the overflow pipe, but does not give a definite warning when the bath is overflowing.

Lavatory basins, Fig 4 May be made from earthenware, fireclay stoneware o vitreous china. The two popular sizes are 559 mm × 406 mm and 635 mm × 457 mm.

Weights (minimum)

	559 mm × 406 mm	635 × 475
Fireclay	20.412 kg	26.308 kg
Earthenware (light)	10.886 kg	13.608 kg
Earthenware (heavy)	14.515 kg	18.144 kg
Vitreous China	14.515 kg	18.144 kg
Stoneware	14.515 kg	18.144 kg

Fixing Basins may be supported on cantilever brackets (built-in or screw-o pedestals, or legs and bracket, or they may be cantilevered from the wall by means of a lug which is part of the basin. The lug is built into the wall with cement and sand mortar.

113

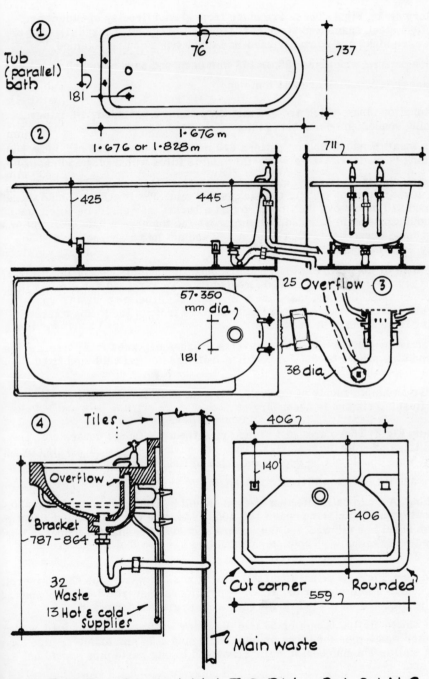

① Tub (parallel) bath

76

737

181

1·676 m

② 1·676 or 1·828 m

425

445

711

57·350 mm dia

181

25 Overflow ③

38 dia

④ Tiles

Overflow

Bracket
787 - 864

32 Waste

13 Hot & cold supplies

Main waste

406

140

406

Cut corner   Rounded

559

BATHS & LAVATORY BASINS

Sinks, Slop Sink and Urinals

Scullery sinks, Fig.1 These are made from glazed fireclay or stoneware, stainless steel, enamelled steel, cast iron or fibreglass. Glazed fireclay or stoneware sinks are normally used, and three types can be obtained.

London pattern, which are 127 or 178 mm deep, and have no overflow.

Belfast pattern, which are 254 mm deep.

Combination sinks, which are 254 mm deep and are provided with integral draining spaces on one or both sides.

For a small house, a Belfast pattern 610 mm × 457 mm × 254 mm most popu
The sink is made with a weir overflow and is fitted with a plug and chain.

The sink should be fixed on cast iron brackets so that the height from the floor level to the top edge of the sink is 889 mm. The brackets should theref
be fixed 610 mm above the floor. So that a bucket may easily be filled, the ho
and cold taps should be fixed 150 mm above the top edge of the sink. The wa
pipe should connect to a back inlet gulley and not into a channel or dished gulley as is often seen.

Slop sinks or hoppers, Fig.3 These are used in hospitals, hotels, institutions etc. They are made from glazed fireclay or stoneware, and are similar to a W.C. in construction and may, like a W.C., be of corbel or pedestal type with S or side outlets. A teak insert is fitted to the front of the fitting to protect tl
glazing from damage by buckets etc.

The brass or gun-metal bucket prevents brushes or swabs from entering the pan and also allows buckets to be filled from the hot and cold taps fixed above.

To give an ample supply of water for removal of filth from the pan a 14 litre flushing cistern is necessary

Urinals, Fig.3 These are used in factories, theatres, public houses etc., and are fittings used by the male sex. They are made from glazed fireclay or sto
ware. Slate should not be used due to risk of flaking and fouling.

There are three types: slab, stall or basin.

Flushing An automatic flushing cistern should be used for this purpose (see automatic flushing cisterns page 105, 106. 4. 54 litre per stall or per 610 mm
of slab should be allowed, and the cistern should fill so that the urinal is flusl
every twenty minutes. The cistern should be fixed so that the underside is about 2 m above the floor level.

Waste pipe, Fig.4 A urinal is a 'soil' fitting and the waste pipe should theref
connect into a soil pipe or drain. On upper floors cast iron, lead or copper may be used and on ground floors cast iron or glazed stoneware.

For a single stall a 38 mm or 50 mm diameter waste pipe is required, a 64 n
diameter waste pipe for three or four stalls, and a 76 mm diameter pipe for
to six stalls. The number of stalls connected to one waste pipe should not exceed six.

115

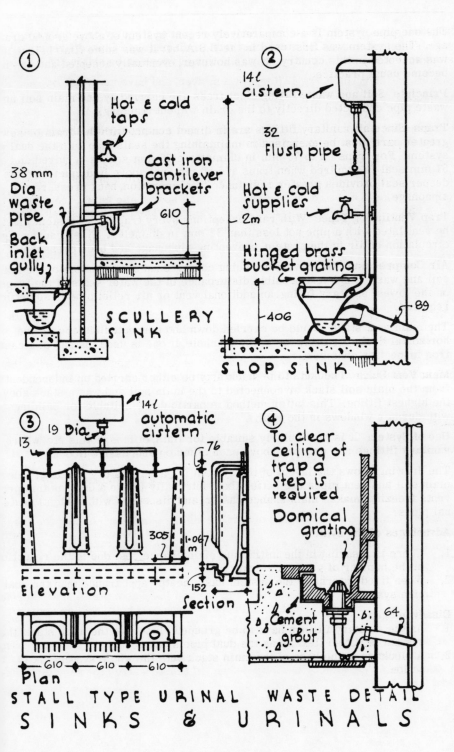

① **SCULLERY SINK**

Hot & cold taps

Cast iron cantilever brackets

610

38 mm Dia waste pipe

Back inlet gully

② **SLOP SINK**

14ℓ cistern

32 Flush pipe

Hot & cold supplies 2m

Hinged brass bucket grating

89

406

③ **STALL TYPE URINAL**

14ℓ automatic cistern

19 Dia

13

305

610 · 610 · 610

Elevation

Plan

76

1·067 m

152

Section

④ **WASTE DETAIL**

To clear ceiling of trap a step is required

Domical grating

Cement grout

64

SINKS & URINALS

One-pipe System

The one pipe system is a comparatively recent system of above ground drai
age. The system was first used in the U.S.A. but it was some time before it
was accepted in this country. It was however, eventually accepted and has n
become usual practice.

Principle Soil and waste fitting discharges are carried by one main soil an
waste pipe connected directly to the drain without trapping.

Traps Since all sanitary fittings are in direct contact with the drain or sew
greater care must be exercised in maintaining the seals than with the dual
system. For traps up to 76 mm in diameter a 76 mm seal is required and a
51 mm seal is required when traps are 76 mm and above in diameter. This
deeper seal provides greater resistance to evaporation, back pressure and
siphonage.

Trap Ventilating Pipes With rare exceptions every trap in the system must
be ventilated with a pipe not less than 32 mm in diameter. This ensures a g
circulation of air in the system, preventing siphonage and back pressure.

Air Compression To prevent air being compressed at the bottom of the mai
soil and waste stack and possible disturbance of the water seals of the traps
on the lowest sanitary fitting, an additonal vent or air relief pipe is sometim
required.

The main vent stack should be carried down and connected either into the
horizontal drain or, at the top of the manhole, if one is used instead of a cast
iron inspection chamber.

Main Vent Stack The end of the stack may be either carried up independentl
from the main soil stack or connected to the main soil and waste stack abov
the highest fitting. This latter method is particularly suitable for buildings
with dormer windows in the roof.

Use of System It is particularly suitable for flats, offices, hotels etc. where
sanitary fittings are grouped above each other on successive floors.

The drawing shows the layout of the system for a three story building. The
main soil and vent pipes are better fixed internally inside a duct, as this pre
vents freezing, makes maintenance easier, and dispenses with unsightly exte
nal pipes.

Advantages of the system

1. There is a saving in the initial and maintenance cost due to the reductio
    in the number of vertical stacks.
2. When fixed externally the system has a neater appearance than the dual
    pipe system.

Disadvantages

1. As the sanitary fittings have to be grouped closely to the main stack, the
    system is not so flexible as the dual pipe system.
2. A blockage in the base of the main stack puts the whole system out of
    action.

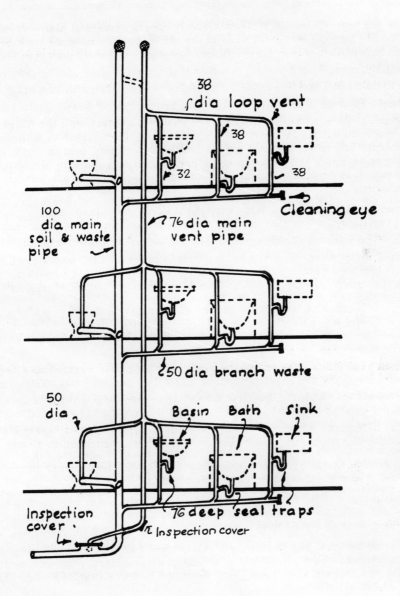

ONE PIPE SYSTEM

The Dual-pipe System

The dual or two pipe system is the oldest of the sanitary systems and the regulations of practically all Local Authorities are based on it. In this system the sanitary fittings are divided into two groups, soil fittings and waste fittings

Soil Fittings These are for the disposal of foul matter and include W.Cs, urinals, slop sinks and bedpan washers etc.

Waste Fittings These are for the disposal mainly of soapy waste water and include baths, showers, lavatory basins, bidets, washtubs, washing fountains et The branch pipes from the soil and waste fittings are connected to separate s and waste stacks, hence the term 'dual pipe system'.

Soil Stack This is connected 'direct' to the drain by means of a bend at the f of the stack. The main points regarding the stack are:

1. The pipe should be carried up to a point 900 mm above the top of any wir dow within a distance of 3 m and carried up without any reduction in diameter.
2. The internal diameter should be not less than the internal diameter of the outlet of any soil fitting discharging into it, and in any case not less than 76 mm.
3. If ranges of W.C.s are installed on each floor, a 50 mm diameter anti-siphon pipe may be required which should be connected to the branch soil pipe not less than 76 mm and not more than 300 mm from the crown of the traps.
4. The top of the pipe should be fitted with a wired copper or galvanised steel cage.
5. A rainwater pipe or gutter should not discharge into the soil pipe unless the drainage is combined.

Waste Stack In some districts waste pipes discharge over a hopper head. Th is not good practice as lengths of fouled waste pipe are exposed to the open air, nearly always below window openings. The stack should be carried up in the same way as a soil pipe and 'disconnected' from the drain by means of a back inlet gully trap. The minimum water seal for the traps is 38 mm and th minimum diameter of the branch pipes 32 mm. The drawing shows a typical dual pipe system for a three storey building.

Advantages of the System Where sanitary fittings are required to be situate at some distance from each other, separate soil or waste stacks may be provided, thus obviating long horizontal runs of pipe to a main stack.

Disadvantages The provision of a separate waste stack increases initial and maintenance cost. When pipes are fixed externally, the number required for the system tend to be unsightly. Larger ducts are required when pipes are fixed internally.

119

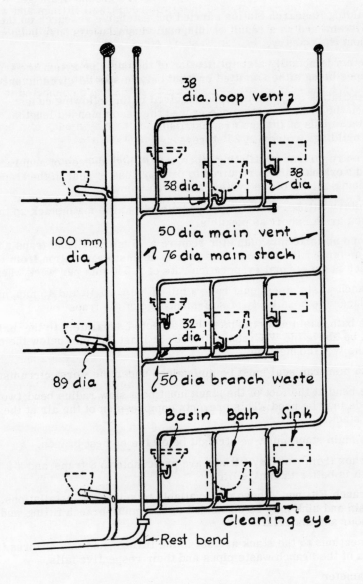

DUAL PIPE SYSTEM

Single Stack System

Modern conditions and the demand for low cost housing drew attention to the need for a simplified but efficient form of above ground drainage.

The Building Research Station carried out extensive research on the 'Single Stack System' and as a result of this, many installations have been made throughout the country.

The system is actually a simplification of the one pipe sytem, the trap ventilating pipes being either omitted or used only in special circumstances.

Trap ventilating may, however, be required in the following cases:
(a)   when the branch waste pipes exceed the recommended lengths.
(b)   when ranges of fittings are installed.
(c)   on buildings exceeding 25 storeys.

As there are no trap ventilating pipes, a very high degree of accuracy in planning and workmanship is required to prevent loss of seal in the traps. The main requirements of the system are given below.

(a)   Sanitary fittings must be grouped closely to the main stack so that branch pipes are as short as possible.

(b)   Traps up to 76 mm diameter require a 76 mm seal, and traps above 76 mm diameter a 50 mm seal. This guards against evaporation from the trap, which has a normal evaporation rate of 2.540 mm per week when not in use.

(c)   Branch waste pipes must have a fall of between 18 and 45 mm/m. This reduces the possibility of self-siphonage of the traps.

(d)   The bath, basin and sink must be connected separately to the main stack, and be above the W.C. connection, or at least 203 mm below the centre line of the W.C. connection.

(e)   A 25 mm trap seal must be maintained under the worst circumstances.

(f)   The bend at the foot of the stack must be a slow radius bend; two 135° bends may be used. This prevents compression of the air at the base of the stack.

(g)   The main stack must be straight below the highest branch.

(h)   P traps from sanitary fittings are preferable to S traps, and a 9 litre flush is better than a 14 litre

Multi Branch Fittings These are available to suit most installations. The W.C. bath, basin and sink may be connected to one multi-branch fitting, and thus save labour and material.

The connections to the stack are set in the fittings, and this ensures the correct positions of the branch waste pipes and their respective falls.

Stack diameter
(a)   76 mm or 89 mm for two storey housing (providing the W.C. outlet does not exceed 76 mm).
(b)   100 mm up to five storeys with two groups of fittings on each floor.
(c)   125 mm up to twelve storeys with one group on each floor or ten storeys with two groups on each floor.
(d)   150 mm up to 20 storeys with two groups on each floor.

Note. A group of fittings consists of W.C. bath, one or two basins and one sink

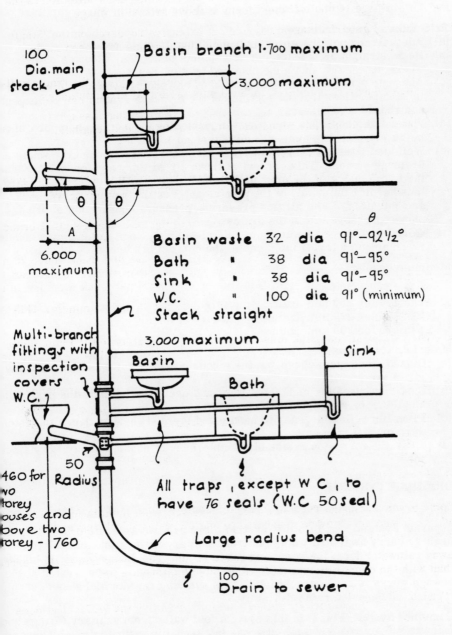

100
Dia.main
stack

Basin branch 1·700 maximum

3.000 maximum

θ   θ

A

6.000
maximum

		θ
Basin waste	32 dia	91°–92½°
Bath "	38 dia	91°–95°
Sink "	38 dia	91°–95°
W.C. "	100 dia	91° (minimum)

Stack straight

Multi-branch
fittings with
inspection
covers
W.C.

3.000 maximum

Basin   Sink

Bath

460 for
two
storey
houses and
above two
storey - 760

50
Radius

All traps, except W C, to
have 76 seals (W.C 50 seal)

Large radius bend

100
Drain to sewer

S I N G L E   S T A C K
S Y S T E M

Simple Domestic Drainage Systems

Definition of a drain The Public Health Act, 1936, defines a drain as a pipe for the drainage of one building or any building within the same curtilage.

Principles of good drainage
(a) Adequate support. A granular bed 100 mm thick is required.

(b) Be as straight as possible between points of access. Changes of directi where necessary, should be obtained by slow bends.

(c) Adequate access. Inspection chambers or rodding eyes should be place in such positions that all sections of the drainage system can be inspec and rodded if necessary.

(d) Water tightness. The whole system, including inspection chambers, sho be watertight. The pipes should withstand 1.2 m head of water.

(e) Well ventilated. A current of fresh air should pass through the whole drainage system. This current of fresh air will dry any foul matter adh ing to the inside of the pipe and this foul matter will be washed forward thus keeping the inside of the pipe clean. Ventilation also prevents accumulation of foul air and preserves pressure equilibrium at atmos- pheric pressure within the drains.

(f) Correct gradient. A minimum self-cleansing velocity of 0.8 m/s shoul be obtained by laying the pipes to the correct gradient.

Minimum gradients

1 in 108 for 100 mm drain
1 in 178 for 150 mm drain
1 in 295 for 229 mm drain
1 in 425 for 300 mm drain

Materials for drains
(a) Glazed stoneware—cheap, but the labour cost for laying is high, as many joints are required.

(b) Cast iron—used for high class work and desirable when drains pass und a building or road.

(c) Pitch fibre—flexible, easy to handle and lay, and cheaper than either stor ware or cast iron pipes.

(d) u.P.V.C.—corrosion resistant, flexible, easy to handle and lay; very smo bore.

DRAINAGE SYSTEMS

Some towns and cities need a 'separate', some a 'combined' system.

Separate System, Fig. 1 In this system there are two separate drains i.e. on drain to carry away foul water etc from sanitary fittings, and another to car away rainwater from the roofs and paved areas. The drainage cost is higher than with the combined system, but the volume of sewage to be treated at the sewage works is considerably less. This system prevents foul gases escapi through an unsealed rainwater gully.

Combined System, Fig. 2 In this system foul water from sanitary fittings an rainwater from roofs and paved areas is carried in a single drain. There is saving in drainage cost but treatment at the sewage works costs more.

123

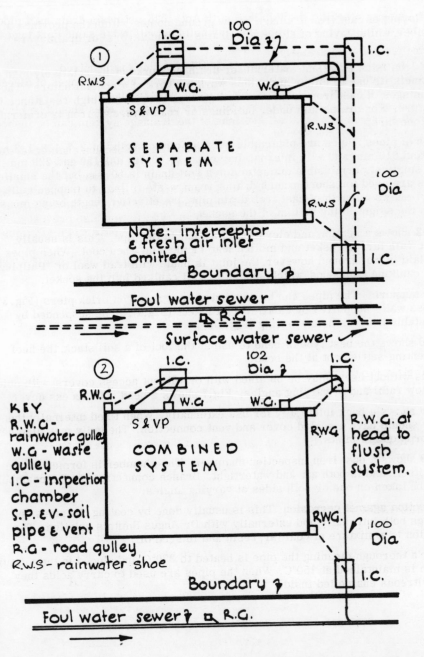

SIMPLE DOMESTIC DRAINAGE SYSTEMS

Within the figure:

(1)
I.C.
100 Dia
I.C.
R.W.S
W.G.
W.G.
S & VP
R.W.S
SEPARATE SYSTEM
100 Dia
R.W.S
R.W.S
Note: interceptor & fresh air inlet omitted
I.C.
Boundary
Foul water sewer
R.G.
Surface water sewer

(2)
I.C.
102 Dia
I.C.
R.W.G.
W.G.
W.G.
S & VP
RWG
COMBINED SYSTEM
R.W.G. at head to flush system.
RWG
100 Dia
I.C.
Boundary
Foul water sewer
R.G.

KEY
R.W.G - rainwater gulley
W.G - waste gulley
I.C - inspection chamber
S.P. & V - soil pipe & vent
R.G - road gulley
R.W.S - rainwater shoe

Cast Iron Drainage

The laying of cast iron drainage below ground comes within the province of the plumber, whilst laying of stoneware drains is bricklayers' or drainlayers' work.

Cast iron is an excellent material for drainage work but its relatively high cost restricts its use to either high class work or work of a special nature. The advantages of cast iron are: fewer and stronger joints, and high resistance to fracture. For drains laid under buildings or roadways, cast iron is preferable to stoneware.

Sizes of pipes Pipes are obtainable with effective lengths of 2.7, 1.8, 1.2 m, 914 and 610 mm and with internal diameters of 50, 76, 100, 150 and 229 mm. The smallest permissible diameter for a soil drain is 50 mm but the smaller sizes are used for short branch drains, from waste fittings to trapped gullies. Fig. 1 shows a length of cast iron drain pipe, the effective length being measured from the spigot to the bottom of the socket.

Fig. 2 shows a section and elevation of a joint in the pipe. This is usually made with tarred gasket and molten lead caulked up when cool. When pipes are laid in wet ground however, the joint is made with lead wool or 'Philplug' cold caulking compound, which should be well caulked into the socket.

Pipe supports The pipes can be carried above ground on brick piers (Fig. 3), across walls supported by cantilever brackets (Fig.4), or be suspended by adjustable hangers below ceiling (Fig.5).

Fig.6 shows the best type of bend to use at the foot of a soil stack, the heel preventing settlement at the bend.

Bends without heels may be obtained with or without access covers, with quick or slow radii and of varying angles. Fig.7 shows a bend with access cover.

Fig.8 shows a back inlet gully for use externally. When fixed internally the gully should have a sealed cover and vent connection. The gully may also have one or two side inlets.

Fig.9 shows a cast iron inspection chamber. The chamber is formed on the pipe itself, and is both air and watertight. Branch connections to the chamber may be taken on one or both sides at varying angles.

Protection against corrosion This is usually done by coating the pipes and fittings both internally and externally with Dr Angus Smith's solution. The solution is a mixture of coal tar, resin and linseed oil.

After a thorough cleaning the pipe is heated to 370°C and dipped in the mixture which is maintained at 150°C. When the pipes are used to carry acids they are vitreous enamelled inside.

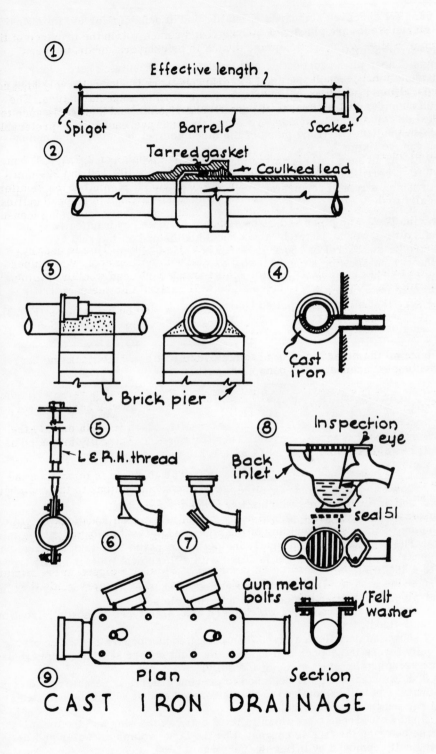

① Effective length
Spigot   Barrel   Socket

② Tarred gasket
Caulked lead

③
Brick pier

④ Cast iron

⑤ L.&R.H. thread

⑧ Inspection eye
Back inlet
seal 51

⑥   ⑦

Gun metal bolts
Felt washer

⑨ Plan   Section

CAST IRON DRAINAGE

Stoneware Drainage

B.S. 65: 1971 specified standards of quality and dimensions for the following salt-glazed stoneware pipes and fittings:

Pipes—Straight pipes
Fittings—Taper pipes, concentric and level invert (eccentric); bends; taper bends; junctions; channels, straight and taper, half-section; channel bends, half-section; channel junctions, half-section.

B.S. 65 requires that pipes and fittings complying with the standard shall be marked as follows:

(a) With the name or trade mark of the manufacturer legibly impressed upon it before fixing
(b) With the licence number of the manufacturer and the B.S. 65/1971.
(c) With a certification mark of **Extra** if the article complies to the higher crushing strength requirement or **Tested** if the article has been hydraulically tested.

Hydraulic Test The pipes and fittings should be tested hydraulically at the manufacturers works. Straight pipes should withstand an internal hydraulic pressure on the barrel of 158 kPa. Fittings should withstand a pressure of 69 kPa without showing signs of injury or leakage. The pressure should be applied at a rate not exceeding 69 kPa in 5 s and full pressure should be maintained for at least 5 s.

Make sure that all air is expelled before starting test.

Lengths of straight pipes and channels

Internal diameter of pipe or channel	Length excluding depth of socket	Permissible variation
Up to and including 203 mm	610 mm, 762 mm, 914 mm or 1.219 m	plus or minus 3.175 mm per 305 mm of length.
229 mm to 914 mm inclusive	914 mm, 1.219 m or 1.524 m	

Fig. 1 shows a straight stoneware pipe; Fig. 2 an ordinary cement joint and Figs 3 and 4 flexible joints which allow ground movement.

To make an ordinary joint, tarred hemp gasket is wrapped round the spigot of each pipe. This assists centring of the pipes and prevents mortar getting into them. The gasket is caulked tightly inside the socket to less than a quarter of the socket depth and the socket is filled with stiff cement mortar neatly trowelled to a 45° fillet.

Fig. 5 shows a back inlet gully for receiving discharges from a waste or rain-water pipe. The hopper has one, two or three inlets.

Fig. 6 shows an interceptor of which there are three types 'cascade', 'freeflow' and 'anti-flood'.

Fig. 7 shows an anti-flood gully. When back flooding occurs the water rising in the gully forces the copper ball against the india rubber seating and prevents water escaping through the top of the gully.

Fig. 8 shows a garage gully designed to prevent silt, oil or petrol from entering the drain. The silt is retained in the perforated bucket whilst the deep water seal retains the oil and petrol.

Fig. 9 shows a grease trap, which is fixed between the sink and the drain. Grease entering the trap is congealed by the large volume of water and is periodically removed by lifting the perforated tray.

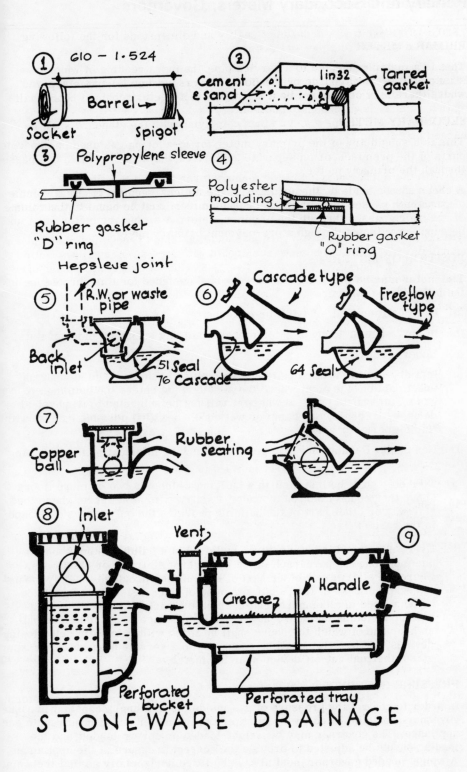

① 610 — 1·524

Barrel →

Socket   Spigot

② Cement e sand   1 in 32   Tarred gasket

③ Polypropylene sleeve

Rubber gasket "D" ring

Hepsleve joint

④ Polyester moulding

Rubber gasket "O" ring

⑤ ↑R.W. or waste pipe

Back inlet

51 Seal
76 Cascade

⑥ Cascade type   Free flow type

64 Seal

⑦ Copper ball   Rubber seating

⑧ Inlet

Perforated bucket

⑨ Vent

Grease   Handle

Perforated tray

STONEWARE DRAINAGE

Primary and Secondary Meters; Governors

PRIMARY METER

This is a meter connected to a service pipe, the index reading of which constitutes the basis of charge by the Board for gas used on the premises, and where there may or may not be a secondary meter.

SECONDARY METER

This is a subsidiary of the primary meter for measuring gas used on separate parts of the premises, or on separate appliances, the whole of which has passed through the primary meter.

A check can be made on the accuracy of the meters, because the total volume of gas which passes through the secondary meter must be equal to the volume of gas which passes through the primary meter. A secondary meter must not be supplied with gas through a pre-payment primary meter.

POSITION OF METER

The meter may be fitted in a meter cupboard designed for this purpose, or in the following positions:

(a) In an entrance hall of a flat or maisonette.

(b) In a passage or lobby of a commercial building such as a block of flats.

(c) Under a staircase.

(d) In a dry well-ventilated building, the meter should be fitted as near as practicable to the point where the service pipe enters the building. A gas meter should be sited where it will not be subjected to (i) physical damage, (ii) continuous damp or wet conditions, (iii) possible contact with flame, sparks or acid.

The Gas Safety Regulations 1972 give the following information for the siting of a gas meter:

(a) No meter shall be installed, in a building which has two or more floors above the ground floor, on or under a stairway or elsewhere, where the stairway or other part of the building provides the only means of escape in the case of fire.

(b) Every meter and its connections, installed in a building other than the one mentioned in paragraph (a) on or under a stairway or elsewhere, where the stairway or other part of the building provides the only means of escape in case of fire, shall either be of fire-resistant construction or be housed in a compartment of which the enclosing sides, top and bottom, including the doors, have a fire resistance of not less than half an hour and of which the doors shall be fitted with automatic self-closing devices, or the meter shall be connected to a service pipe which incorporates a thermal cut-off device near the meter.

PRESSURE GOVERNOR

In order to control the pressure of gas inside the building, a constant pressure governor should be fitted on the inlet pipe to the meter and if required, to each appliance. The governor may be weight-loaded or spring-loaded, and the loading should be adjusted to provide the correct pressure at the appliances. A weight-loaded governor must always be fitted horizontally so that the weight

129

acts vertically on the diaphragm. Spring-loaded governors may be fitted in any position and are therefore more popular than the weight-loaded types.

A section through a spring-loaded constant pressure governor is shown, which operates as follows:

a) Gas enters the governor at inlet pressure and passes through valve A to the appliance and also through the bypass to space B between the two diaphragms.

b) The main diaphragm is loaded by the spring and the upward and downward forces acting on the diaphragm are balanced. The upward and downward forces acting on the compensating diaphragm are also balanced and this has a stabilising effect on the valve and counteracts any tendency to oscillation.

c) Any fluctuation of inlet pressure will inflate or deflate the main diaphragm, thus raising or lowering valve A and altering the resistance to the flow of gas, and thus ensuring a constant pressure at the outlet to the appliance.

Note. The space above the large diaphragm is ventilated to atmosphere to allow unrestricted movement of the valve. The diaphragms may be made from rubber, leather or plastics. A filter may be fitted on the inlet to the governor.

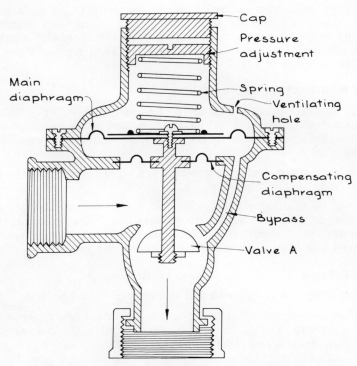

NOTE - SCREWING DOWN THE PRESSURE ADJUSTMENT INCREASES THE OUTLET PRESSURE

SPRING-LOADED CONSTANT PRESSURE GAS GOVERNOR

Gas Service Pipes and Automatic Control

MATERIALS USED FOR PIPES

Lead and lead alloy Is most suitable for short connections to meters, the flexibility of the pipe prevents strain on the meter and appliance connections.

Copper Is excellent for the complete installation, the pipes having a smooth internal bore, being neat in appearance, very durable and giving some degree of flexibility at the meter and appliance connections.

Mild steel Is cheaper than lead and copper and more rigid. This is an advantage where damage to the pipes has to be considered and where pipes have to be hung from the ceiling. Class A pipes should not be used, Class B may be used for installation pipes and Class C for service pipes.

SERVICE PIPE, Fig. 1

This is the pipe between the undertakings main and the main gas cock inside the building. It should never be less than 25 mm internal dia.

Method of laying The pipe should be laid 375 mm below ground and have a steady fall back to the main so that condensation will fall back to the main.

INSTALLATION PIPE, Fig. 2

This includes every pipe from the outlet side of the meter to the appliances. The pipes should have a steady fall back to the meter. If the main is above the meter, a siphon box or condensate receiver should be fitted to the service pipe. The box is emptied by a pump connected to the suction pipe. Pipes are connected to the meter as in Fig. 3.

U GAUGE OR MANOMETER, Fig. 4

This is used to measure the gas pressure or test for leakage. When the rubber tube is connected to a gas tap and the tap is turned on the pressure of the gas forces the water up the U tube as shown, thus indicating this pressure in mm water gauge.

To test for leakage all but one of the gas taps are closed and to this the U gauge is connected.

Air is blown into the installation until 300 mm or twice the working pressure is obtained. The gauge is then left for 10 minutes and if after a further 15 minutes the water remains still, then the installation is sound. Any leakage should be traced with soap solution applied to joints by a brush.

THERMOSTAT, Fig. 5

Used to control temperature in ovens and storage type water heaters.

Operation When the oven or water becomes hot, the brass tube expands and carries with it the invar rod which expands very slightly. The rod brings the valve closer to its seating and reduces the flow of gas.

BI-METAL STRIP, Fig. 6

Operates the pilot safety device for Ascot water heaters; it shuts off the burner's main gas supply when the pilot flame is extinguished.

Operation When the pilot flame is lit the bi-metal strip is heated and the brass expands about 18 times more than the invar. This causes the strip to bend in wards and open the main gas valve.

131

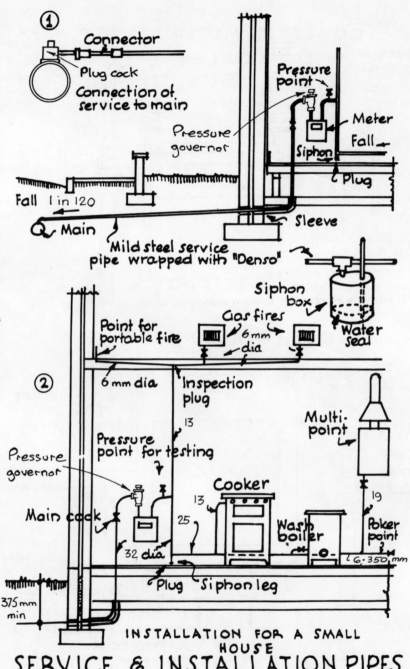

① Connector

Plug cock

Connection of service to main

Pressure point

Pressure governor

Meter

Fall

Siphon

Plug

Fall 1 in 120

Main

Sleeve

Mild steel service pipe wrapped with "Denso"

Siphon box

Gas fires

Water seal

Point for portable fire

6 mm dia

6 mm dia

② Inspection plug

Multi-point

13

Pressure governor

Pressure point for testing

13

Cooker

19

Main cock

25

Wash boiler

Poker point

32 dia

6·350 mm

Plug Siphon leg

375 mm min

INSTALLATION FOR A SMALL HOUSE

SERVICE & INSTALLATION PIPES

③

DOMESTIC METER

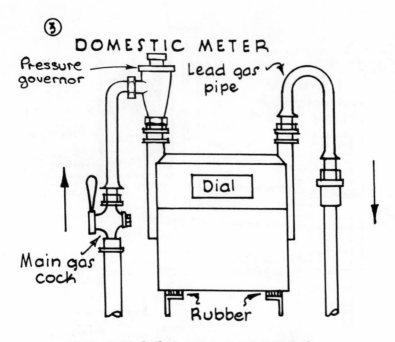

Pressure governor · Lead gas pipe

Dial

Main gas cock

Rubber

INDUSTRIAL METER

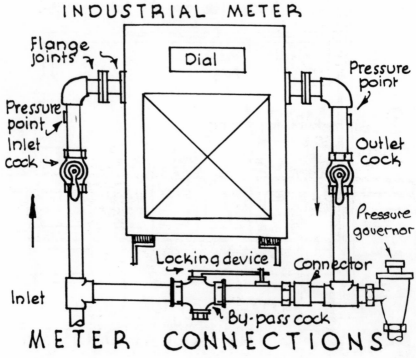

Flange joints

Pressure point

Pressure point
Inlet cock

Dial

Pressure point

Outlet cock

Pressure governor

Inlet

Locking device

Connector

By-pass cock

METER CONNECTIONS

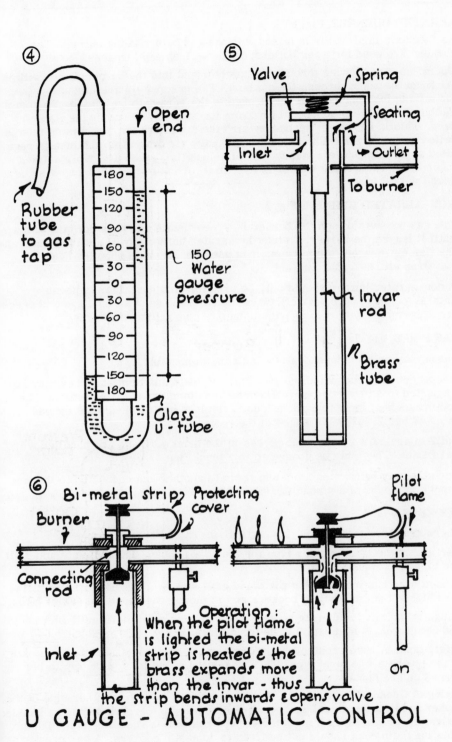

④

Open end

Rubber tube to gas tap

180
150
120
90
60
30
0
30
60
90
120
150
180

150 Water gauge pressure

Glass U-tube

⑤ Valve   Spring   Seating

Inlet   Outlet

To burner

Invar rod

Brass tube

⑥ Bi-metal strip Protecting cover

Burner

Pilot flame

Connecting rod

Inlet

On

Operation: When the pilot flame is lighted the bi-metal strip is heated & the brass expands more than the invar - thus the strip bends inwards & opens valve

U GAUGE - AUTOMATIC CONTROL

Gas Burners, Fires and Cookers

AERATED BURNERS, Fig. 1

As the name implies air is mixed with the gas before being burned. These burners are used for wash boilers, cookers, fires and furnaces.

Operation Gas flowing through the injector and into the burner draws with it air from the room through the air port. The gas and air are mixed together i the mixing tube before passing through to the burner to be ignited. To comple the burning process additional air from the space surrounding the flame is used. This is known as 'secondary air'; the air drawn into the mixing tube is called 'primary air'. The amount of primary air drawn into the tube is regulated so as to produce a steady, non-luminous flame with a sharply defined inner cone. An aerated burner is essential for natural gas but may also be used for coal gas.

NON-AERATED BURNER, Fig. 2

The gas passes through the burner in a 'neat' state and does not mix with air until it leaves the burner. Unlike the aerated burner it will not light back, and the flame produced is luminous. It is used for all types of water heaters, gas fires etc.

A non-aerated burner should only be used for coal gas. This is because natural gas has approximately twice the calorific value of coal gas and needs air to be mixed with it to provide complete combustion of the gas.

GAS FIRES, Fig. 3

These may be (a) independent, (b) built in, (c) portable.

Independent are supported independently as the name implies. They may be connected to a brick flue or be flueless and standing on a tiled hearth. The continuous heat input to a room from a flueless heater should not exceed 146.5 W per 2.831 m^3 of space in the room.

Built-in are built in a special recess in the brickwork and are panelled with flat fronts. They may be connected to a brick flue or be flueless.

Portable may be carried from one room to another and connected to the gas supply by means of a strong flexible tube.

COOKERS, Fig. 4

There are three main types: (a) vertical, (b) raised oven (c) range.

Vertical is the most popular type for the small house. The hot plate and grill are placed above the oven.

Raised oven has the oven, hot plate and grill side by side. The oven is therefore higher than in vertical cookers and is more convenient and easier to use.

Range is the most elaborate cooker incorporating a hot plate, grill, storage and hot closet. It is most suitable for a large family.

Safety taps. All taps controlling burners which do not light automatically are of the 'push-in-and turn' type. This makes it impossible for the tap to be turned on accidentally.

Fixing of Cookers A space of 102-152 mm should be left on either side of the cooker to allow for cleaning; the fixing of cookers in corners should be avoided A flexible 13 mm or 19 mm diameter pipe connection should be made but an isolating main cock should not be fixed to domestic cookers. A gas pressure governor is sometimes supplied with cookers and fires.

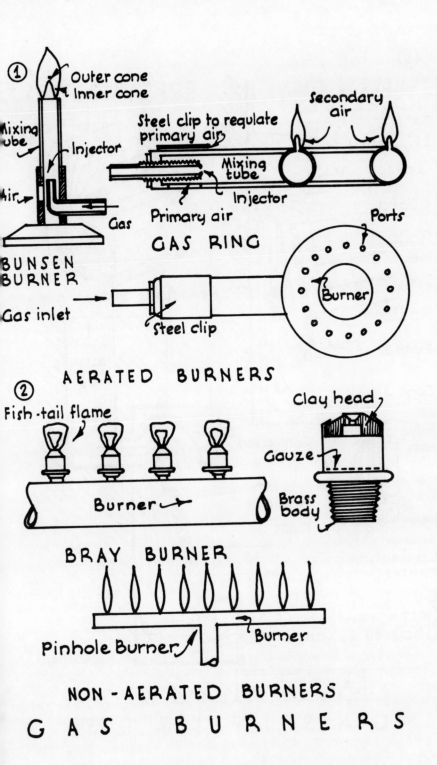

① Outer cone
   Inner cone

Mixing tube

Injector

Air

Gas

BUNSEN BURNER

Steel clip to regulate primary air

Mixing tube

Injector

Primary air

Secondary air

GAS RING

Gas inlet

Steel clip

Ports

Burner

AERATED BURNERS

② Fish-tail flame

Burner

BRAY BURNER

Clay head

Gauze

Brass body

Pinhole Burner

Burner

NON - AERATED BURNERS

GAS BURNERS

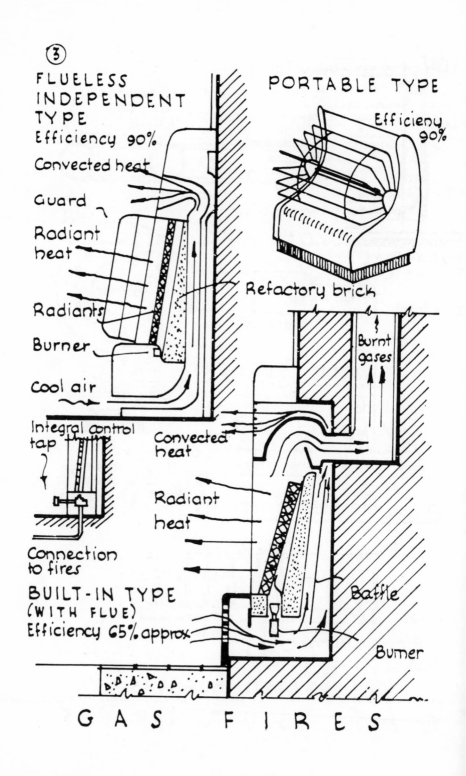

(3)

FLUELESS
INDEPENDENT
TYPE
Efficiency 90%

Convected heat

Guard

Radiant
heat

Radiants

Burner

Cool air

Integral control
tap

Connection
to fires

BUILT-IN TYPE
(WITH FLUE)
Efficiency 65% approx.

PORTABLE TYPE

Efficiency
90%

Refactory brick

Burnt
gases

Convected
heat

Radiant
heat

Baffle

Burner

G A S   F I R E S

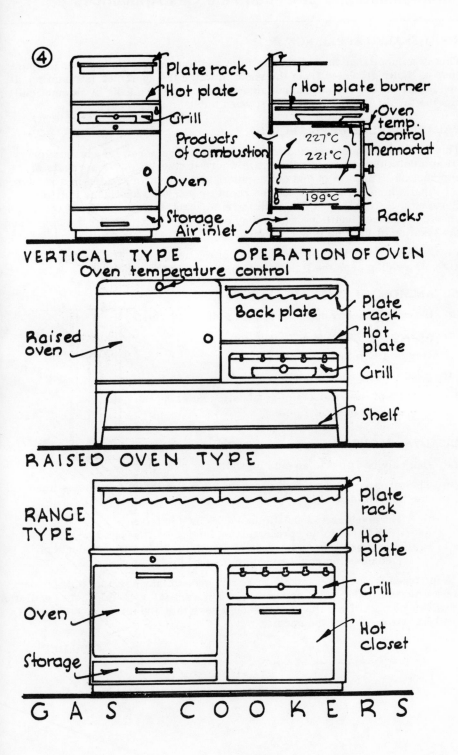

④

Vertical Type
- Plate rack
- Hot plate
- Grill
- Products of combustion
- Oven
- Storage
- Air inlet

Operation of Oven
- Hot plate burner
- Oven temp. control
- Thermostat
- 227°C
- 221°C
- 199°C
- Racks

VERTICAL TYPE   OPERATION OF OVEN

Raised Oven Type
- Oven temperature control
- Raised oven
- Back plate
- Plate rack
- Hot plate
- Grill
- Shelf

RAISED OVEN TYPE

Range Type
- Plate rack
- Hot plate
- Grill
- Hot closet
- Oven
- Storage

RANGE TYPE

GAS COOKERS

Room-sealed and Balanced Flue Gas Appliances

ROOM-SEALED APPLIANCE, fig. 1

This is an appliance having the air inlet and flue outlets (except for the purpose of lighting) sealed from the room in which the appliance is installed. It includes a drying cabinet having an access door, with means of automatically closing the air inlet and flue outlet when the door is opened.

BALANCED FLUE APPLIANCE, fig. 2

This is an appliance designed to draw in the air required for combustion from a point immediately adjacent to where it discharges its products of combustion. These inlet and outlet points must be incorporated in a windproof terminal, which is sited outside the room in which the appliance is fitted. Because the air inlet and flue outlet are adjacent, any variations of the atmospheric pressure conditions which may occur have an equal effect on each and the function of the flue is not affected.

Fig. 3 shows the principle of operation of the appliance. The column of cool air outside displaces the lighter hot gases inside the appliance.

ADVANTAGES OF BOTH APPLIANCES

(a)   Higher efficiency due to less heat loss in the flue.

(b)   No need for an expensive long flue.

(c)   May be fitted in a confined space.

(d)   Less risk of condensation.

(e)   No risk of the products of combustion entering the room.

(f)   Neat in appearance.

DISADVANTAGES

(a)   Can only be fitted to an outside wall.

(b)   The terminal may present some problem and the following positions must be avoided:

> (i) immediately beneath the eaves or a balcony.
> (ii) adjacent to any projection on the face of the building
> (iii) at a position on the face of a building where the products of combustion could re-enter the building.

Note. When the outlet is wholly or partly beneath any opening—e.g. any part of a window capable of being opened, or any ventilator, or inlet to a ventilation system—no part of the flue outlet should be within 300 mm, measured vertically, of the bottom of the opening.

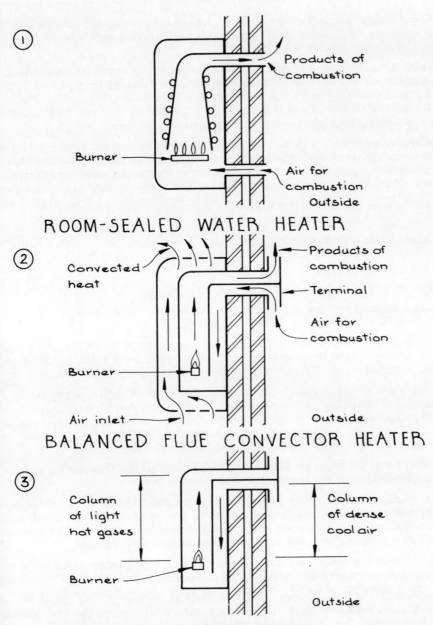

① **ROOM-SEALED WATER HEATER**

- Products of combustion
- Burner
- Air for combustion
- Outside

② **BALANCED FLUE CONVECTOR HEATER**

- Products of combustion
- Convected heat
- Terminal
- Air for combustion
- Burner
- Air inlet
- Outside

③ **PRINCIPLE OF OPERATION**

- Column of light hot gases
- Column of dense cool air
- Burner
- Outside

ROOM-SEALED AND BALANCED FLUE
GAS APPLIANCES

Gas Flues

The purpose of a gas flue is either to remove the products of combustion f
the appliance or to serve both this purpose and provide ventilation for the
room where the appliance is installed.

Size of flues For perfect combustion 10 m^3 of air is required for every 1
of gas burned and the flue must be designed accordingly. Size ranges of fl
are fine 100 mm-203 mm dia, circulators 76 mm-89 mm dia, bath water he
100 mm-152 mm dia, wash boilers 89 mm dia, storage heaters 89 mm, the
size depending upon purposes and heat input of appliance.

Materials for flues Galvanised mild steel, asbestos cement, brick or refra
tory concrete is used. Brick or concrete is usual for internal flues; either
is preferable to mild steel or asbestos cement, normally used for external
flues. Flues should be constructed for the following gas appliances:

Space heating appliances having a continuous heat input exceeding 146.5 W
per 2.8 m^3 of room space.

Instantaneous bath water heaters and any other appliance fitted in a bathroo
for heating bath water having a heat input exceeding 146.5 W per 1.000 m^3
of room space.

Wash boilers etc. whose heat input exceeds 5860 W.

Central heating boilers Storage water heaters, Hot water boilers and circu
lators with a heat input of 4395 W or more.

Design of flues, Fig. 1 A gas flue normally consists of the following four pa
the primary flue, which may form part of the appliance e.g. multipoint heate
the draught diverter; the secondary flue or flue proper; the terminal.

The draught diverter is fitted to prevent a 'down blow' from extinguishing t
flame and thus prevents gas entering the room. If a down blow occurs, the
flue gases which are non-toxic are deflected outside the appliance. Provide
that the condition does not persist long enough to affect the freshness of the
air entering the appliance, there will be no harmful effects.

The terminal prevents birds nesting in and blocking the flue and the entry o
rain. It minimises the possibility of a 'down draught'.

Termination of flues 'High pressure' regions should be avoided for the ter
ination of flues. These regions are directly above or underneath the eaves,
in the corner of a building or close to a projection such as a soil pipe or att
ched pier. Fig. 2 shows the best positions for flue terminations.

Fig. 3 shows the construction of a precast refractory concrete flue for a 7-
storey building where room-sealed appliances must be used.

Condensation in flues Water vapour forms a large part of flue gases, and s
of it will condense in the flue if the temperature falls below the dew point o
the flue gases. For this reason internal flues are better than external ones,
because the flue is kept warm.

Fig. 4 shows a method of dealing with condensate. A union near the flue bas
is necessary for clearing the pipe should a blockage occur.

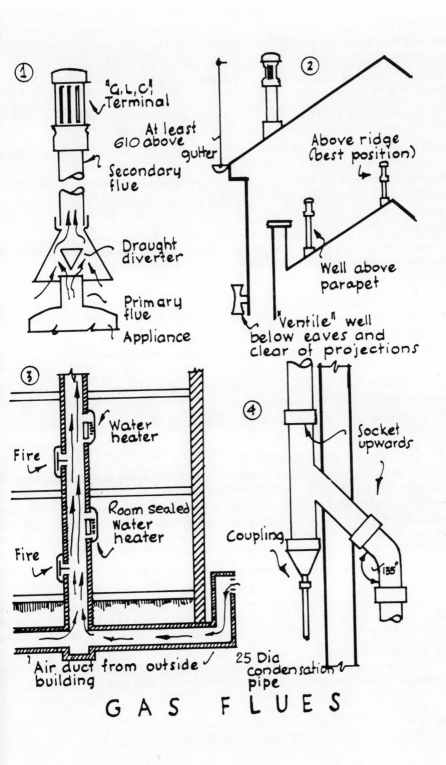

① "G.L.C" Terminal

At least 610 above gutter

Secondary flue

Draught diverter

Primary flue

Appliance

② Above ridge (best position)

Well above parapet

"Ventile" well below eaves and clear of projections

③ Water heater

Fire

Room sealed Water heater

Fire

Air duct from outside building

④ Socket upwards

Coupling

135°

25 Dia condensation pipe

GAS FLUES

Gas Water Heaters

There are three main types of gas water heaters: instantaneous, storage and circulator.

INSTANTANEOUS HEATERS

These give instant hot water, the water being heated as it passes through the heater by a finned heat exchanger. Instantaneous heaters may be divided into four classes:

Sink heaters which may be either single or multipoint to serve a sink or a sink and lavatory basin. They are fitted with a swivel spout outlet.

Bath heaters which are fitted with a swivel spout outlet to serve a bath and lavatory basin.

Boiling water heaters which provide hot or boiling water for tea brewing.

Multipoint Instantaneous heaters which may be connected to a bath, basin or sink.

Fig. 1 shows a method of connecting a multipoint instantaneous heater to an existing hot water system. To obtain hot water from the heater, stop valve F is closed and stop valve A is closed and stop valve B is opened.

STORAGE HEATERS

The hot water is stored in an insulated vessel. There are 2 classes of storage heaters.

Storage Multipoint Heater which may be connected to bath, basin and sink. The heater may be supplied with cold water from a cistern integral with the heater or from a separate storage cistern.

Storage Sink Heaters are provided with a swivel spout outlet. They may be supplied direct from the main or from a storage cistern.

Fig. 2 shows the method of installing a hot water system using a multipoint storage heater.

CIRCULATORS

These heaters are connected to the hot water storage cylinder or tank with a flow and return pipe. The heater may provide the sole means of providing hot water or be used as a booster to a solid fuel boiler.

Fig. 3 shows a circulator connected to a hot water storage cylinder to provide the sole means of obtaining hot water.

Fig. 4 shows a circulator connected to an existing hot water supply system.

CALCULATION OF GAS CONSUMPTION

The amount of gas consumed in m^3/hr may be found from the following formula

$$m^3/s = \frac{Power}{Calorific\ value} = \frac{kW}{kJ/m^3}$$

The calorific or heating value of town gas ranges from about $16\,785\ kJ/m^3$ to $20\,555\ kJ/m^3$ while natural gas gives about $37\,300\ kJ/m^3$.

Assuming a calorific value of $18\,650\ kJ/m^3$ then a sink water heater with a heat input of 11.72 kW would require $11.72 \div 18650 = 0.00063\ m^3/s$ or $2.265\ m^3/hr$.

The therm $= 105.506$ MJ.

The efficiency of heaters when new ranges from 75-80 per cent.

143

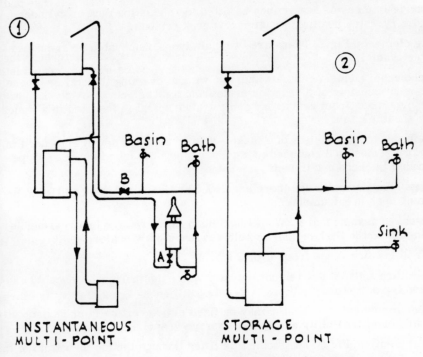

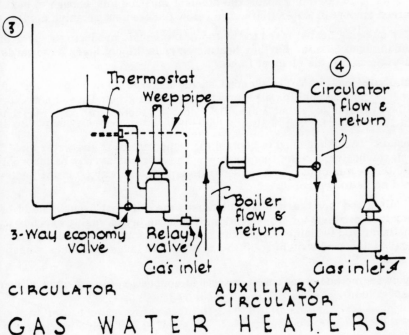

GAS WATER HEATERS

Electric Immersion Heaters

An electric immersion heater may be fitted to an existing tank or cylinder for auxiliary water heating in summer or peak periods.

Heating elements, Fig.1 There are two main types, removable or embedded (non-removable).

The removable element can be withdrawn without draining the storage vessel. The element consists of a resistor made from a nickel-chrome spiral, mounted on supports made from refractory cement. The spiral is inserted in a tinned copper sheathing tube.

The embedded type consists of a nickel-chrome resistor spiral embedded in refractory cement and enclosed in a copper tube. The tube is bent to shape, brazed into the head and tinned.

Loadings For domestic use there are 250, 500, 1000, 1500, 2000 and 3000 W depending upon requirements.

It is usual to assume that 1 kW will heat 45.5 litre of water in a reasonable time, so that a 136 litre cylinder would require a 3 kW heater.

Industrial heaters range from 4 to 12 kW.

Temperature setting For temporary hard water the thermostat should be set 60°C and for soft water 70°C.

Position of element The heater may be fixed either vertically or horizontally depending on accessibility and type of storage vessel.

Vertical position, Fig.2 The element is fitted through the top or bottom of the storage vessel. In the top position, the element must be long enough to heat the required amount of water (the water below the element remains cold).

The water on being heated rises to the top of the vessel producing a layer of hot water in about 20 min. Further heating extends the hot layer downwards until all water above the element is hot.

Horizontal position, Fig.3 The element should be fixed 50 mm above the bottom of the vessel. In this position all the water is heated gradually and hot water will not be available for about 2 hrs. Fig.4 shows a method of fixing horizontally which provides hot water after a few minutes.

Thermostats These are used to control the temperature of the water and switch off the heater at a set temperature. The thermostat may be incorporated with the heater or it may be a separate unit, fixed away from the heater and wired so as to control it.

Fig.5 shows a rod type thermostat which uses the different expansions of brass and invar (nickel steel) for its operation. When the brass casing expands it pulls the invar rod (which expands only slightly) with it, thus breaking an electrical contact and switching off the heater. The magnet ensures a snap-action break.

Fig.6 shows a method of making a watertight connection for a heater without the use of solder.

①

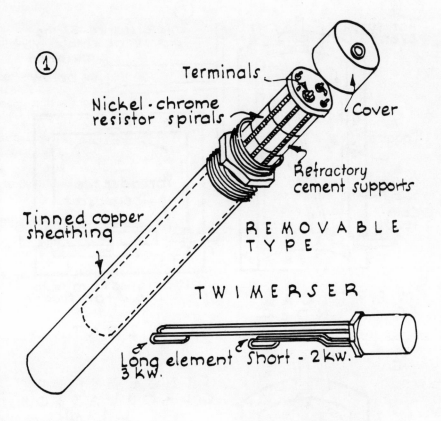

Terminals

Nickel·chrome
resistor spirals

Cover

Refractory
cement supports

Tinned copper
sheathing

R E M O V A B L E
T Y P E

T W I M E R S E R

Long element   Short - 2 kw.
3 kw.

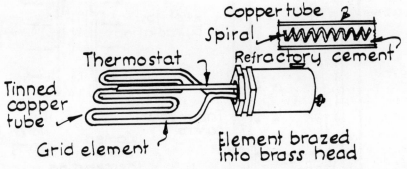

Copper tube

Spiral

Refractory cement

Thermostat

Tinned
copper
tube

Grid element

Element brazed
into brass head

N O N - R E M O V A B L E   T Y P E

I M M E R S I O N   H E A T E R S

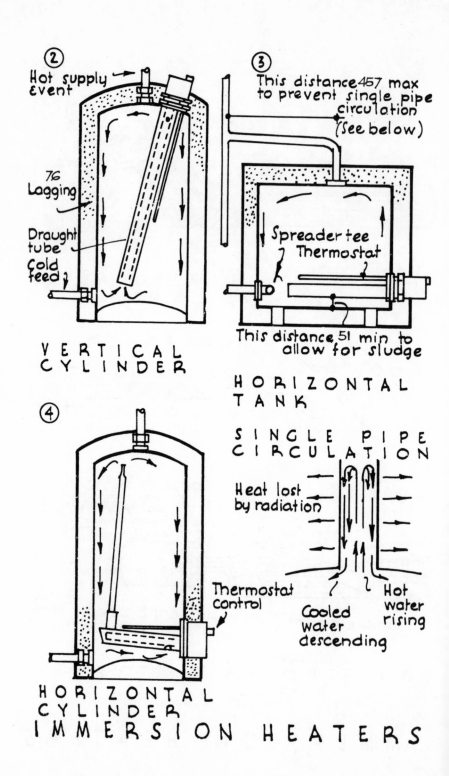

② Hot supply event

76 Lagging

Draught tube

Cold feed

V E R T I C A L
C Y L I N D E R

③ This distance 457 max to prevent single pipe circulation (See below)

Spreader tee
Thermostat

This distance 51 min to allow for sludge

H O R I Z O N T A L
T A N K

S I N G L E   P I P E
C I R C U L A T I O N

Heat lost by radiation

Cooled water descending

Hot water rising

④ Thermostat control

H O R I Z O N T A L
C Y L I N D E R
I M M E R S I O N   H E A T E R S

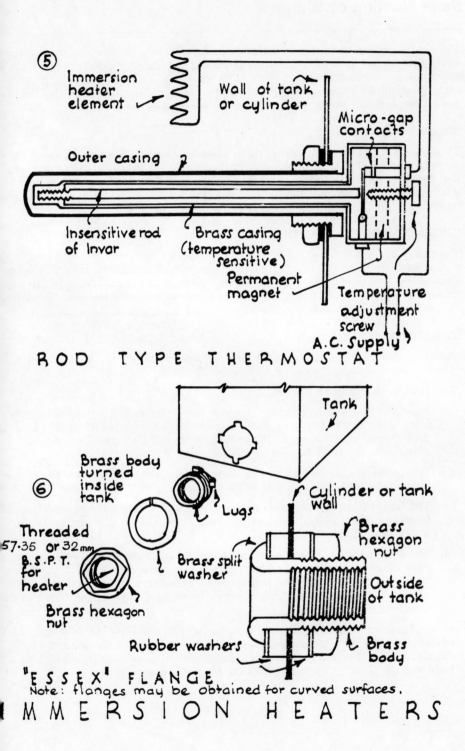

⑤ Immersion heater element

Wall of tank or cylinder

Micro-gap contacts

Outer casing

Insensitive rod of Invar

Brass casing (temperature sensitive)

Permanent magnet

Temperature adjustment screw

A.C. Supply

ROD TYPE THERMOSTAT

Tank

Brass body turned inside tank

⑥

Lugs

Cylinder or tank wall

Threaded 57·35 or 32mm B.S.P.T. for heater

Brass hexagon nut

Brass split washer

Brass hexagon nut

Outside of tank

Rubber washers

Brass body

"ESSEX" FLANGE
Note: flanges may be obtained for curved surfaces.

IMMERSION HEATERS

Solar Heating of Water

The heating of water by use of a flat plate solar collector sited on the roof ma save up to 40 per cent of the heating costs for hot water supply. The flat plate solar collector should have an area of between 4 and 6 m² and be fixed at an angle of about 40° facing south. A collector facing south-west is preferable to one facing south or south-east but any southern aspect is suitable.

SOLAR COLLECTOR, fig. 1

This consists of an aluminium alloy or copper frame with a sealed glass cove A copper or steel collector, painted matt black, is fixed inside the frame so that there is an air space of about 20 mm between the glass and the collector Aluminium foil is fixed at the back of the collector and 75 to 100 mm of glass fibre or foamed plastic insulation is fixed behind the foil.

OPERATION OF COLLECTOR

The glass cover allows about 90 per cent of higher temperature short wave radiation from the Sun to be transmitted through it, but allows less than 10 pe cent of the lower temperature long wave radiation to escape. This is often called the 'greenhouse effect' and ensures that solar radiation is collected ar is not lost again by outward radiation.

THE SOLAR SYSTEM, fig. 2

The fluid flowing through the solar heating side of the system consists of a mixture of water and non-toxic antifreeze.

The system operates as follows:

(a) The flat plate solar collector is heated by solar radiation which in turn heats the mixture of water and antifreeze to a temperature of 50 to 60 °C On a sunny day in summer it is possible for all the hot water for an average house to be heated by the solar panel.

(b) The pump is switched on by the control box when the temperature of the thermostat at A exceeds that of the thermostat at B by between 2 and 3 °

(c) The liquid from the solar collector is pumped through the heat exchange fixed inside the 200 litre solar cylinder. The heat exchanger heats the water in the solar cylinder.

(d) When hot water is required to be drawn off through the hot water taps, th cold water from the cold water storage cistern forces the hot water from the solar cylinder into the conventional cylinder and thus reduces or eliminates the heat required to raise the temperature of the water in the conventional cylinder.

Note. In order to prevent loss of fluid in the solar part of the system it is sealed, but the expansion vessel takes up the expansion of the water. The expansion vessel contains a rubber diaphragm with one side in contact with t fluid and the other in contact with a cushion of nitrogen gas.

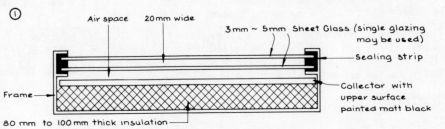

① Air space   20mm wide   3mm ~ 5mm Sheet Glass (single glazing may be used)

Sealing strip

Frame

Collector with upper surface painted matt black

80 mm to 100 mm thick insulation

SECTION THROUGH SOLAR COLLECTOR

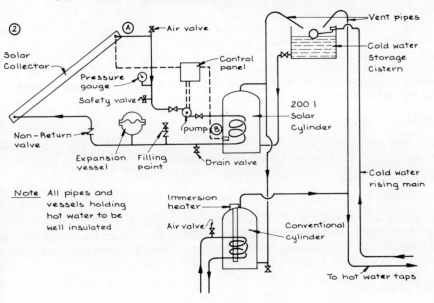

② Air valve   Vent pipes

Solar Collector

A

Control panel

Cold water Storage Cistern

Pressure gauge

Safety valve

200 l Solar Cylinder

pump B

Non-Return valve

Cold water rising main

Expansion vessel   Filling point   Drain valve

Note All pipes and vessels holding hot water to be well insulated

Immersion heater

Air valve

Conventional cylinder

To hot water taps

DETAIL OF A SOLAR HEATING SYSTEM
SOLAR HEATING OF WATER

Solar Space Heating

By providing good insulation, including double glazing throughout, a house m
be provided with a solar space heating system.

A solar flat plate collector on the roof of the house, facing south, may be us
to heat water inside an insulated tank installed below ground. For a house
having a total floor area of 150 m², a solar collector having an area of 40 m
to heat 40 m³ of water has been found satisfactory and over 200 kW of heat
be stored and released for space heating when required.

The tank is spherical and is made from glass fibre. Insulated with two laye
of glass fibre and polythene, it is buried below the ground on a 300 mm bed
clinker filter media. Further filter media is enclosed in a polythene lining
and is packed around the tank for at least 600 mm.

CONTROLS

The panel primary system is provided with two pumps, and an alarm system
in the event of failure. Electrically operated two-way valves are used to
divert the flow from the hot water cylinder to the heat storage tank. The ri
of overheating the water in the heat storage tank is dealt with by the use of
a 13 mm bore cold feed pipe connected to the bottom of the tank. Water pas
through the pipe is controlled by a thermostatic valve which opens when the
temperature of water in the tank is too high. In this event the cold water flo
into the tank and forces hot water out of an overflow pipe to waste. The san
system is used to top up the tank should a float switch indicate that there ha
been a loss of water

PRIMARY SYSTEM

The whole of the primary system is operated on a 30 per cent glycol-water
mix which will not freeze in winter. The system is sealed and an expansion
vessel takes up the expansion of the fluid when heated.

SPACE HEATING SYSTEM

The output coil at the top of the tank is connected to a 15 kW fan convector
heater positioned underneath the floor. Ducting carries warm air to the
various rooms of the house. If required, underfloor panel heating may be
used with plastic or copper pipe coils.

PERFORMANCE

The system is estimated to provide about 70 per cent of the energy requirements for hot water supply and between 30 and 40 per cent of the energy
requirements for space heating.

DOMESTIC HOT WATER

A well-insulated 337.5 litre combination cylinder is installed inside the airi
cupboard. The cylinder contains a large solar coil at the lower part and a
small coil for conventional heating from a boiler at the top part.

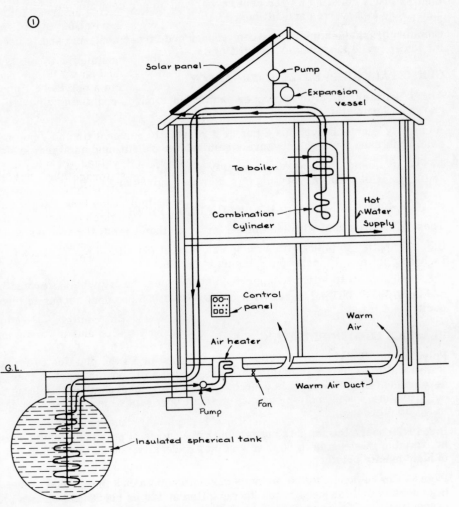

SOLAR SPACE HEATING

B.S.1400 Brasses and Gunmetals; Plastics

BRASSES (COPPER-ZINC ALLOYS)

Admiralty brass contains 70 per cent copper, 29 per cent zinc and 1 per cent tin. The tin content improves its resistance to corrosion, particularly by sea water.

English brass contains 64 per cent copper and 36 per cent zinc and is used for high grade taps, valves and fittings.

Common brass contains 50 per cent copper and 50 per cent zinc and is used for lower grade taps, valves, and fittings.

GUNMETALS (COPPER-ZINC-TIN ALLOY)

A true bronze is an alloy of copper and tin but bronzes containing zinc are known as 'gunmetals'.

Admiralty gunmetal contains 8 per cent copper, 10 per cent tin and 2 per cent zinc. It is used for high pressure steam valves and fittings.

Leaded gunmetal contains 85 per cent copper, with 5 per cent each of tin, zinc and lead. It is used for very high grade water valves and fittings.

B.S. 602, 1085: 1970—LEAD AND LEAD ALLOY PIPES

These standards deal with lead pipes for other than chemical purposes.

B.S. 602 applies to pipes with a composition of at least 99.8 per cent lead and including antimony, zinc, copper, bismuth and tin.

B.S. 1085 applies to silver-copper-lead alloy pipes, the alloy being formed by adding 0.003-0.005 per cent silver and 0.003-0.005 per cent copper to high purity lead.

PLASTICS USED IN PLUMBING

Polyethylene (Polythene) Polythene was the first of all the plastics to replace traditional materials in plumbing and has played an important part in the development of plastics. It is used for cold water pipes, particularly in agricultural work where mole ploughing of small bore pipes may be used for laying in suitable ground.

B.S. 1972 covers the weights and working pressures of polythene tubing which is available in sizes up to 50 mm bore in low density, and up to 300 mm bore in high density polythene.

Pages 21 to 24 describe the methods of jointing and bending polythene tubes. High density and low density polythene soften at 120 to 130 °C and 85 to 87 °C respectively.

Polyvinyl chloride (P.V.C.) Unplasticised polyvinyl chloride (u.P.V.C.) is used for cold water pipes, ventilating ducts, rainwater gutters and pipes, and drainage systems. The softening temperature of P.V.C. is 75 to 82 °C and is therefore unsuitable for hot water pipes, but it may be used for taking short periods of discharge of hot water.

Water pipes may be joined by a solvent cement applied to both the socket of a u.P.V.C. fitting and the end of the pipe. The end of the pipe is then pushed into the socket of the fitting and the two mating surfaces weld together.

Drainage pipes may be joined by means of a rubber sealing ring inside the socket of the pipe. This is known as the 'push-fit' joint.

153

Polypropylene This plastic is used for small bore waste and ventilating pipes up to 50 mm bore. The softening temperature is 130 to 150 °C and is therefore very suitable for waste traps.

The plastic cannot be solvent cemented so a rubber sealing ring inside the socket of the fitting is used. The plastic is also used for valves, siphons, and cold water cisterns.

Nylon The softening temperature of this plastic, about 180 °C, makes it suitable for heating and hot water pipes. It is also used for moulded valves and bearing surfaces. Pipes may be joined by means of a special brass compression fitting.

Polystyrene In its expanded form, as a cellular material, it is used extensively as a thermal insulator.

Polytetrafluoroethylene (P.T.F.E.) Used as a jointing tape which is wrapped around the threads of the pipes instead of hemp and jointing paste.

Perspex Used for baths, wash basins, sinks and shower trays. A perspex bath supplied with a cradle in wood or metal as an integral part of the unit and perspex panels may be used for enclosing the bath.

Sanitary fittings made from perspex are easy to clean, are light in weight and may be obtained in a variety of colours. The colour penetrates right through the thickness of the material.

Perspex possesses a high degree of chemical resistance and highly corrosive chemicals such as bleaches have no injurious effect on the material. Hot utensils and burning cigarette ends should not be placed in contact with perspex which, because of its thermoplastic characteristics, is affected by temperature in excess of 120 °C.

Acrylonitrile butadiene styrene (A.B.S.) Used for small size waste and ventilating pipes of up to 50 mm bore. The softening point of A.B.S. is 93 to 150 °C and is therefore suitable for taking short periods of discharge of hot water. Jointing may be accomplished by means of either a rubber jointing ring or solvent cement.